Arla

BLUE DIAMOND ALMONDS
Almond Breeze

CAKESMITHS
THE COFFEE SHOP CAKE SPECIALISTS

E EXTRACT COFFEE ROASTERS

H & J

Olam Specialty Coffee

Victoria Arduino
1905

FOR BREW
FREAKS,
BEAN
GEEKS
AND THE
SIMPLY
CURIOUS ...

www.saltmedia.co.uk
Tel: 01271 859299
Email: ideas@saltmedia.co.uk

Salt Media *Independent Coffee Guide* team:
Richard Bailey, Nick Cooper, Clare Hunt, Kathryn Lewis,
Abi Manning, Tamsin Powell, Jo Rees, Rosanna Rothery,
Amy Sargeant, Christopher Sheppard, Dale Stiling, Mark Tibbles,
Selena Young, Josephine Walbank and Lara Watson.

Design and illustration: Salt Media

A big thank you to the *Independent Coffee Guide* committee
(meet them on page 230) for their expertise and enthusiasm, our
headline sponsors KeepCup and Yeo Valley and sponsors Arla,
Blue Diamond Almonds, Cakesmiths, Extract Coffee Roasters,
Henny & Joe's, Olam Specialty Coffee and Victoria Arduino.

Coffee shops, cafes and roasteries are invited to be included
in the guide based on meeting strict criteria set by the
committee, which includes the use of speciality beans,
providing a high quality coffee experience for visitors and being
independently owned.

For information on *Independent Coffee Guides for* Ireland,
Scotland and North, Midlands & North Wales, visit:

www.indycoffee.guide

f 🐦 📷 @indycoffeeguide

PELICANO

COFFEE CO.

Nº43
Pelicano Coffee Co. – Queens Road

contents

WELCOME

№04
Our Place — Get the Boys a Lift

It's been a cracking year for the speciality coffee scene and I'm thrilled to welcome you to the newly extended *South England & South Wales Independent Coffee Guide*.

In this edition we've cast the net even wider in our search for phenomenal caffeine experiences. And, in addition to covering the South West and South Wales, the *Indy Coffee* team have combed the south coast across to Sussex and journeyed into caffeine-rich Oxfordshire.

On our travels through this slice of the British Isles, we've witnessed the heightened awareness of sustainability and spoken to baristas and coffee shop owners who are introducing eco initiatives. Roasters are also assessing their green credentials – turn to page 14 to find out about some of the changemakers at the front of the curve.

As ever, each venue included in the guide has exceeded the strict quality criteria for inclusion and been given the thumbs up by our committee of coffee pros – meet them on page 230.

We can't wait to hear what you think of the new guide; keep us up to date with your favourite finds on social.

Kathryn Lewis
Editor
Indy Coffee Guides

 @indycoffeeguide

The evolution of an icon

Introducing KeepCup Thermal.
Double-walled, vacuum sealed
stainless steel for lasting
drinking pleasure on the go.

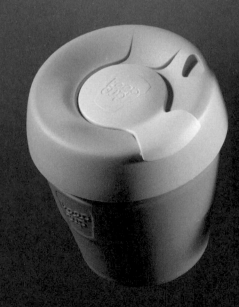

GREEN BEANS

The shift in attitude towards sustainability has seen speciality coffee shops upping their eco creds, but how do the indie roasteries that supply the beans measure up? **Kathryn Lewis** unearthed some initiatives greening-up the roasting process

While many speciality coffee fans champion ecologically responsible activities such as the introduction of reusable cups, the use of local or alt milks and a zero-tolerance approach to food waste, many are still in the dark when it comes to the carbon footprint of the beans used in their morning flat white. Should they be concerned?

TECH ATTACK

'Broadly speaking, coffee roasting produces fairly low levels of emissions compared to other elements such as milk production,' says Bradley Steenkamp, co-founder of Horsham Coffee Roaster in West Sussex.

'However, without proper treatment, coffee roasters emit particulate matter and volatile organic compounds which aren't good for general health. To control the release of these compounds into the atmosphere, a roaster needs to be fitted with either an afterburner or an electrostatic filter.

'Afterburners are very effective but unfortunately need a significant amount of gas to operate and therefore emit an increased amount of CO2.'

Aware of their impact on the planet, a growing number of speciality roasters such as Bradley are introducing tech designed to reduce roastery emissions.

'At Horsham we've invested in a Loring S35. By recirculating hot air from the burner/afterburner, the roaster saves as much as 80 per cent on gas use, which we saw first-hand when we switched from a traditional drum roaster. We estimate that we currently save about 4,000kg of LPG (liquid petroleum gas) and 12,000kg of CO2 per year,' says Bradley.

REUSE AND RECYCLE

It's not just technology that's cleaning up the coffee roasting process. Instead of buying new machines, progressive roasteries such as Extract Coffee Roasters in Bristol are saving vintage models from landfill and restoring them with added (efficiency-focused) extras.

'Ten years ago we rescued a 1955 cast iron Probat roaster in a state of disrepair,' says Extract co-founder David Faulkner. 'Naming her Betty, we carefully restored and brought her back to life.

'This set us on a path that's shaped Extract's entire ethos: built not bought, rescuing and upcycling old rather than buying new.

'The next project was a 120kg Probat roaster (Bertha) which we found as a pile of parts in Bosnia and completely rebuilt over four years.'

'These restorations have focused not just on fixing the old machines to avoid waste but also on improving efficiency. Bertha, for example, runs on just 40 per cent of the fuel required for a much newer machine,' says David.

CREATIVE CARBON REDUCTION

While roasting tech and restoration are surefire ways of reducing carbon output, there are other measures roasters can adopt to improve their green credentials. Yallah Coffee in Cornwall is a pioneer in this regard.

'From the early days of Yallah, we've done everything we can to reduce our carbon footprint,' says co-founder Richard Blake.

'We've always calculated our carbon emissions and offset them via a charity called Trees for Life which plants native trees in Scotland.'

'We've also made great efforts to reduce our resource expenditure and have a biomass boiler which produces all our heating and hot water, as well as solar panels which generate pretty much all of our energy. We have a zero-landfill policy and all our by-products – including packaging – are used by a local permaculture farm.'

By-products of the roasting process aren't something most coffee drinkers devote much thought to, yet chaff (the dried husks which detach during roasting) and used coffee grounds are both produced in large quantities.

Savvy Cornish roastery Sabins Small Batch Roasters is putting spent coffee grounds (picked up from their customers) to good use by turning them into eco firelighters.

In South Wales, Afan Coffee Co. has collaborated with local brewery Tomos Watkin to produce a limited-edition coffee stout made using the waste coffee pucks from its roastery-cafe.

PACKAGING PROS

Single-use plastic has become a hot topic and, as awareness of the pollution problem has increased, many roasters have introduced biodegradable or compostable packaging. However, as with "eco" take-out ware, as alternatives become more commonplace their sustainability is being questioned.

'There's a huge problem with the greenwashing of products and materials claiming to be biodegradable, oxo-degradable, omni-degradable, marine-degradable or degradable,' says Tobias Taylor of Devon's Voyager Coffee. *'Whether it's intentional or not, it's confusing for everybody.'*

One of the issues around the use of such packaging is the lack of facilities to recycle it properly. Most compostable packaging, for example, needs to be disposed of in an industrial composter yet many councils in the UK don't have the appropriate infrastructure, so plant-based plastics end up joining everything else in landfill.

Happily, some roasteries like Voyager are looking at truly sustainable alternatives.

"A NEW CIRCULAR SYSTEM ... PACKAGING IS NOW MADE COMPLETELY FROM PLANTS"

'We've introduced a new circular system and our packaging is now made completely from plants,' says Tobias. *'The production of our new bags has a much smaller carbon footprint and its entirety can be composted. We're then closing the loop by recycling our customers' bags at our Dartmoor roastery.'*

Also tackling packaging disposal is Horsham Coffee Roaster, which has rolled out an achievable recycling scheme.

'Our bags are fully recyclable but unfortunately some local councils don't recycle them correctly,' says Bradley. *'So we have a TerraCycle collection box at the roastery and at Bond St. Coffee in Brighton, which means customers can return bags and TerraCycle will turn them into second-use products.'*

There's also been an increase in roasteries delivering their speciality-grade beans in reusable tins and tubs, removing the need to recycle the packaging. One such business is Jericho Coffee Traders in Oxford.

'We're keen to get as many of our customers as possible to bring in their own tubs when they want to restock their supply of Jericho beans,' says Lou Webster.

'We love it when they bring empty supermarket coffee containers; it's great to see how their coffee-buying habits are changing as they support a local, independent business and reduce their plastic and carbon footprint at the same time.'

TRACTION FOR ACTION

While it's inspiring to hear of early adopters at roastery level, as with the wider climate emergency, meaningful change requires collective action.

We need the big players to clean up their acts because the speciality sector comprises just a small slice of the coffee industry. However, as with the big chains' adoption of flat whites and move towards lighter roasts, they usually follow where the indies lead. Let's turn up the heat and encourage them to act more sustainably.

LOVELY FARM SHOP MILK

WITHOUT GOING TO A FARM SHOP

Our 100% Organic milk is sourced from British dairy farms, delivering great tasting consistent quality and addressing the growing demand on transparency, fairness and sustainability.

- No nasty chemicals
- Sourced from cows who are only fed Organic feed
- 30% more plant species on an Organic farm
- Creates biodiversity

WHOLE MILK

Our creamiest milk with all the fat, delivering that delicious taste your customers love. Perfect for full-bodied, full-flavoured coffee, creating a long-lasting foam.

STOCK UP ON THE UK'S No1 ORGANIC DAIRY BRAND!*
FIND OUT MORE AT ARLAPRO.COM

Yeo Valley
ORGANIC

STEP INTO MY COFFICE

Spend your days grafting away in a dull office? Recent studies suggest we get more done when fired up with coffee, cake and connectivity, so maybe it's time to embrace your inner digital nomad, suggests **Rosanna Rothery**

Once, it was the flash of the photocopier, the bubble of the water cooler and the incessant ringing of phones that formed the backdrop to working life. Today, it's just as likely to be the gurgle of milk being steamed, the comforting hum of chatter and the glorious scent of freshly ground coffee.

The number of self-employed workers is steadily increasing and, if the Office for National Statistics is reading its crystal ball correctly, by next year half of UK employees will work remotely in some shape or form.

That means more freelancers than ever will be seeking out work-friendly cafes and coffee bars where they can tap away on laptops while fuelled by caffeine and droolworthy bakes.

Of course, those blessed with the resources might join co-working hubs or check in to private members' clubs. And there'll always be a few self-disciplined types who can work from home without being distracted by domestic chores or taking "restorative" naps.

A good proportion of us, however, are likely to make a beeline for cafes which offer unlimited Wifi, ample table space, plenty of power sockets and   crucially – superb coffee.

'Half of UK employees will work remotely'

Laptops and lattes

Indy Coffee Guide editor and regular remote worker Kathryn Lewis knows just how reassuring the thrumming soundscape of these laptop-friendly cafes can be.

'There's something comforting about the buzz of a coffee shop: the hiss of steam from the espresso machine, the rhythmic whirr of the grinder and the occasional clink of cups,' she says.

'Working from home can get lonely, especially in winter when it's often dark when you open and then finally close your laptop, so cafes can be a great place to get some graft done.'

If your office is wherever you can get instant access to email, the addition of a comprehensive coffee menu and friendly service is not to be underestimated.

'Baristas are often up for a chat and it's good to get some real social interaction as, while speaking to someone over the phone or communicating by email is fine, being able to read someone's smile gives you a natural dopamine boost,' Kathryn adds.

Caffeine and creativity

A busy cafe, on the face of it, might not seem conducive to producing high quality (or quantities of) work, but research has shown that a moderate level of background noise can actually improve performance in creative tasks – and many people testify to the brain-boosting effects of caffeine. There's even a website to help people replicate a cafe's humming soundscape at home: Coffitivity (www.coffitivity.com) plays ambient noise recorded in coffee shops which it claims will 'boost your creativity and help you work better'.

Simon Oxenham, writing in *New Scientist*, cites another reason why people work more effectively in busy places:

'We've known about the audience effect – that having a small audience improves performance – for close to 100 years ... A recent study [also] suggests that mental effort is contagious – simply being around people who are working hard is enough to make us work harder ourselves.'

Coffee and collabs

The coffee shop isn't just an inspiration zone for individuals. It also encourages creative collabs according to Jon Roberts, owner of Quarters Coffee in Newport.

'We have purposely worked hard to provide an atmosphere where creatives and freelancers can feel part of our busy little community,' he says. *'We introduce people to one another all the time and it has been a pleasure to see collaborations happen off the back of laptop users sitting next to each other and finding common ground.'*

By offering space for workshops, masterclasses and evening seminars, Quarters does its best to facilitate new networks in the city.

'The last thing we wanted was to create a place where 20 people sit with their laptops out and headphones on,' says Jon. 'We wanted our coffee shop to act in a small way as a buzzing co-working space where freelancers interact with each other, drink great coffee and feel a sense of belonging that lone working often lacks.'

To make their coffee shop as freelancer-friendly as possible, Jon and co introduced unlimited drinks for a set price.

'From a business point of view, it probably didn't make sense to outsiders, but it has attracted a crowd of young creatives. Lone workers often host meetings in our space which brings in new faces and increased revenue, and creatives tend to be active on social media so they often share photos of what they ate, drank and experienced in our coffee shop.

'Of course, the odd person may take the unlimited deal seriously and slam 14 double espressos before lunch, but most will only have two or three throughout the day.'

'Territorially laying out their laptop, smartphone and iPad while nursing a single cappuccino for hours'

Talk not tech

Not all coffee shops, however, want to be seen as an extension of the office or library. The Missing Bean in Oxford, a popular hangout for both lecturers and students, has eschewed Wifi to encourage imbibers to kick back, socialise and have a rollicking good time.

'We built a big table for co-working at our roastery-cafe, but we didn't feel this would be the right thing for our snug coffee shop in the winding lanes of Oxford,' says creative director Ori Halup. *'Instead we opted for small tables and loud music, in keeping with a sociable atmosphere which students seek out during their library breaks. A row of laptops would really kill the buzzy vibe.'*

Espresso and etiquette

Many of us will have witnessed laptop-wielding "cafe conquerors" who set up their entire office at a table (territorially laying out their laptop, smartphone and iPad) while nursing a single cappuccino for hours. Nobody wants to be that guy, although Kathryn reassures that laptop etiquette is just a matter of common sense.

'It's simple really,' she says. *'Don't take up a four-seater table just to be close to a plug; don't trail your charger across the cafe; don't nurse a single flat white for five hours; don't make loud work calls; do offer to share a table with a fellow freelancer; and, if it's not clear whether laptops are allowed, ask.'*

While acknowledging all that the coffice has to offer (amazing coffee, badass brunches, a buzzy atmosphere, enhanced creativity and cake), she warns it is possible to have too much of a good thing.

'I quickly learnt that working at a coffee shop can induce regular caffeine shakes and sugar crashes. Pace yourself – and maybe go for a decaf and a salad every now and then.'

THE UK'S MOST EXCITING COFFEE SUBSCRIPTION

'Connects independent roasters and coffee fans via the best barista-approved beans' The Independent

Indy Coffee Box will send you a carefully curated selection of speciality beans each month.

Order now at
WWW.INDYCOFFEEBOX.CO.UK

AS FEATURED IN
Olive Magazine, The Independent
Food Magazine, Mountain Biking UK and Off Menu.

HOW TO USE

THE GUIDE

№129
Foundation Coffee Roasters

CAFES

Find coffee shops and cafes where you can drink top-notch speciality coffee. We've split the region into areas to help you find places near you.

ROASTERIES

Discover leading speciality coffee roasteries and find out where to source beans to use at home. Find them after the cafes in each area.

MAPS

Every member cafe and roastery has a number so you can find them either on the area map at the start of each section, or on the more detailed city maps.

MORE GOOD STUFF

Discover more good coffee shops and more good roasteries at the back of the book.

Don't forget to let us know how you get on as you explore the speciality cafes and roasteries.

f 🐦 📷 @indycoffeeguide

WWW.INDYCOFFEE.GUIDE

YOUR ADVENTURE STARTS HERE

№84
Extract Coffee Roasters

SOUTH WALES

Nº21
Bean & Bread

We are a card only
establishment,
thank you.

CAFES

1 Dyfi Roastery
2 The Gourmet Pig
3 unsunghero
4 Our Place – Get The Boys A Lift
5 Alleyway Coffee
6 Mumbles Coffee
7 Square Peg
8 BASEKAMP
9 96 Degrees Speciality Coffee
20 Quarters Coffee
21 Bean & Bread

ROASTERIES

22 Afan Coffee Co.

*All locations are approximate

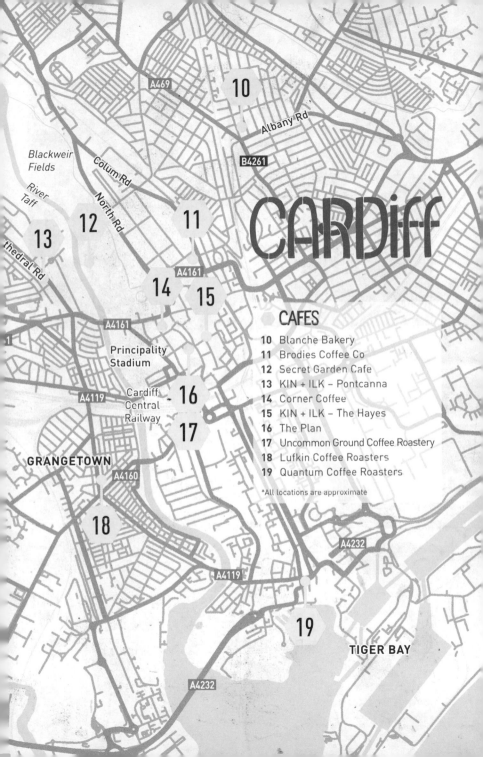

MAP 1 DYFI ROASTERY

29 Heol Maengwyn, Machynlleth, Powys, SY20 8EB

Speciality coffee shops in rural Mid Wales are few and far between, so when you learn about one located in the heart of a UNESCO Biosphere Reserve it's worth planning a visit.

This isn't just a coffee shop in a picturesque setting however: Dyfi Roastery is also a micro-roastery and lifestyle store focused on provenance, where everything from the seeded loaves to the ceramic cups are chosen with care.

TIP LOVE THE DECOR? FIXTURES AND FITTINGS ARE SOLD OFF WHEN THE SHOP CHANGES STYLE

The own-roasted 'Ready For More' beans are joined by a variety of seasonal guests (including Origin, Square Mile and Method) and the baristas have a hefty selection of brewing kit at their disposal. They're a friendly bunch so ask which method best suits your bean of choice.

Delicious cakes and cream teas are rustled up in the Roastery kitchen using fresh ingredients – and any visit should finish with a snoop around the nicely curated array of local pottery, gifts and one-off pieces.

ESTABLISHED
2018

KEY ROASTER
Dyfi Roastery

BREWING METHOD
Espresso, AeroPress, V60, batch filter, french press

MACHINE
La Marzocco Linea PB ABR

GRINDER
Mythos One, Mahlkonig EK43T, Wilfa Svart, hand grinder

OPENING HOURS
Wed-Sat 9am-5pm
Sun 10am-4pm

 Gluten FREE

 BEANS AVAILABLE INSTORE

 WIFI

 CYCLE FRIENDLY

 OUTDOOR seating

 BRING YOUR OWN Cup

 COFFEE COURSES

 DOG FRIENDLY

www.dyfiroastery.com   T: 01654 703947

f @dyfiroasters   🐦 @dyfiroasters   📷 @dyfiroasters

MAP 2 THE GOURMET PIG

32 West Street, Fishguard, Pembrokeshire, SA65 9AD

This upmarket continental-style deli and coffee shop is perfectly positioned for people watching. From seats at the reclaimed-wood window bar (or, if it's fine, at an outdoor table) visitors can drink in the atmosphere of the coastal town while sipping a silky espresso-based coffee.

This year has seen some major changes at The Gourmet Pig as, after a decade of trading, founder Ray Lerwill has added a roasting arm to his popular cafe.

TIP THE NEW ETHIOPIAN SIDAMO GUEST COFFEE IS ALL SWEET AND JUICY STRAWBERRY WITH MILD ACIDITY

Fairtrade organic beans from Honduras and Peru are cooked up on-site in a retro shed and the resulting house blend yields nutty, sweet and fruity notes. The guest spot on the grinder is usually taken by similarly ethically minded Welsh roaster, Coaltown.

In addition to quality coffee, the Pig is loved for its array of local produce. Sample the best of Pembrokeshire – from locally cured charcuterie to award winning cheeses – in a delicious ciabatta and chase it with a slice of something sweet from the counter. And definitely don't leave without a haul of goodies to restock your wine rack and fridge.

ESTABLISHED
2009

KEY ROASTER
Gourmet Pig
Coffee Co

BREWING METHOD
Espresso

MACHINE
La Marzocco

GRINDER
Mazzer Super
Jolly

OPENING HOURS
Mon-Thu **9.30**am-**5.30**pm
Fri **9.30**am-**6.30**pm
Sat **9.30**am-**4.30**pm
Sun **10**am-**3**pm

 Gluten FREE

 BEANS AVAILABLE INSTORE

 WIFI

 CYCLE FRIENDLY

 OUTDOOR seating

 DISABLED ACCESS

 BRING YOUR OWN Cup

---

www.gourmetpig.co.uk   T: 01348 874404

 f @gourmetpig   🐦 @gourmetpig   📷 @gourmetpigcoffeeco

MAP 3 UNSUNGHERO

28a High Street, St Davids, Haverfordwest, Pembrokeshire, SA62 6SD

Surf, skate and coffee culture collide in a beautiful mashup at this St Davids find. And, while it may have been an unsung hero when it first opened in 2013, now a pre- or post-surf unsunghero coffee hit is the norm for anyone visiting this coastline when the waves are good.

The coffee bar sits among the boards, wetsuits and gear at this Pembrokeshire find, creating a unique blended scent of coffee, neoprene and surf wax.

Beans from London's Dark Arts and Workshop feature regularly while roasteries including Herefordshire's James Gourmet and Bath's Colonna have carved out a place on the guest coffee list.

TIP CHECK OUT THE VAST ARRAY OF CLASSIC AND PERFORMANCE SURFBOARDS

The band of baristas specialise in espresso-based drinks so, should you plump for a piccolo, flat white or long black, you're guaranteed a killer cup. Filter fans are not entirely left out though as the shop also stocks AeroPress and V60s for home brewing.

New this year is a blossoming bunch of alternative milks: alongside local and organic dairy varieties, oat and soy are also available.

ESTABLISHED
2013

KEY ROASTER
Multiple roasters

BREWING METHOD
Espresso

MACHINE
Fracino Classic

GRINDER
Mahlkonig E65

OPENING HOURS
Mon-Sun 9am-5pm
(reduced in winter)

www.unsungherosurf.co.uk   T: 01437 729437

f @unsungherosurf   🐦 @unsungherosurf   @unsungherosurf

MAP 4

OUR PLACE – GET THE BOYS A LIFT

7a Dew Street, Haverfordwest, Pembrokeshire, SA61 1ST

'Coffee: it sure as hell isn't the answer ... but f*ck, it helps' is the fruity affirmation to be found at this Pembrokeshire espresso bar, retail shop and drop-in centre.

The gang behind not-for-profit outfit Get The Boys A Lift launched Our Place in 2019 as an open-to-all HQ where they could provide counselling and support services for the local community, sell merch and serve top notch coffee to raise funds for the cause.

Ordering a jumper or beanie online is an easy way to support the movement, but the most delicious option is to pay them a visit for a brew and slice of cake. NZ originals Allpress supply the goods for the La Marzocco machine and the team have been schooled by the roastery's pro trainers in how to pull a mean espresso.

TIP CHECK OUT HOUSE MAG, HITCHER, TO FIND OUT MORE ABOUT GTBAL

Keep the good vibes flowing by donating a coffee or tea forward to someone who needs it via the Oh, Bryn What's Brewing board. Forgotten your wallet? Choose something someone has already donated from the washing-line of drinks and treats.

ESTABLISHED
2019

KEY ROASTER
Allpress Espresso

BREWING METHOD
Espresso, filter, cold brew

MACHINE
La Marzocco Linea Classic

GRINDER
Victoria Arduino

OPENING HOURS
Mon Fri **7.30**am-**4**pm
Sat **7.30**am-**1**pm

BEANS AVAILABLE / INSTORE

WIFI

CYCLE FRIENDLY

DISABLED ACCESS

BRING YOUR OWN CUP

DOG FRIENDLY

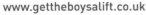

www.gettheboysalift.co.uk

f @gettheboysalift 🐦 @gettheboysalift 📷 @gettheboysalift

№5 ALLEYWAY COFFEE

Guildhall Square, Carmarthen, Carmarthenshire, SA31 1PN

Baristas often reserve their top-shelf beans for filter brew methods, so it's exciting to find a coffee shop that also treats espresso lovers to the special stuff.

A Mahlkonig grinder, La Marzocco machine and the steady hand of a pro barista are the only tools needed to craft exceptional coffee at Alleyway in Carmarthen. The team (headed up by founder Tom Connolly) are so passionate about espresso that they took all other brew methods off the menu – bar the occasional drip special in summer.

Their decision hasn't slimmed down the choice, however, as up to five different beans are available at any time. Roasts from house favourites James Gourmet and Colonna usually sit alongside guests from other UK indies that have caught the team's attention.

TIP LOVE THE CUPS? FIND DAVID'S CERAMICS IN THE RETAIL SELECTION

The pared-back interior, welcoming vibe and record player spinning nostalgic tunes make it easy to unwind while savouring the intricate flavour notes of your pick. Hand-thrown cups and tableware by local ceramicist David Small add to the sensory experience.

ESTABLISHED
2017

KEY ROASTER
Multiple roasters

BREWING METHOD
Espresso, cold brew

MACHINE
La Marzocco Linea Classic

GRINDER
Mahlkonig EK43

OPENING HOURS
Mon-Sat 9am-5pm

Gluten FREE

BEANS AVAILABLE INSTORE

WIFI

CYCLE FRIENDLY

OUTDOOR seating

BRING YOUR OWN CUP

COFFEE COURSES

DOG FRIENDLY

T: 07933 996423
f @alleywaycoffee **◎** @alleywaycoffee

MAP 6 MUMBLES COFFEE

1-3 Castleton Walk Arcade, 26 Newton Road, Mumbles, Swansea, SA3 4AX

Coffee shops worth leaving the Coast Path for come few and far between in South Wales, so be sure to mark this Mumbles stop off on your map.

Take a ten-minute detour from the beach into town to find Mumbles Coffee within Castleton Walk Arcade. It's a hidden-away haven for walkers well-versed in speciality coffee who want to take an hour out with a flat white and fresh-out-of-the-oven bostock (the delicious love-child of french toast and almond croissant).

A recent refurb and expansion of the cosy space has allowed the team to grow the retail section and the new open-plan set-up encourages customers to select and grind their own coffee to brew at home. There's a good choice of single origins and blends to pick from, too, courtesy of roasters such as Extract.

INSIDERS TIP LOOK OUT FOR MUMBLES COFFEE POP-UPS AT VENUES ACROSS SOUTH WALES

If you're not sure where to start, the friendly staff will fill you in on the best brewing equipment, grind size and origins – just be sure to only buy what you can carry home on the trail

ESTABLISHED
2013

KEY ROASTER
Extract Coffee Roasters

BREWING METHOD
Espresso, filter, V60, AeroPress

MACHINE
Sanremo Café Racer

GRINDER
Mahlkonig K30 twin, Mahlkonig E65S, Mahlkonig Guatemala

OPENING HOURS
Mon-Sat **7.30**am-**5**pm

 Gluten FREE

 BEANS AVAILABLE INSTORE

 WIFI

 CYCLE FRIENDLY

 OUTDOOR seating

 DISABLED ACCESS

 BRING YOUR OWN Cup

 DOG FRIENDLY

www.mumblescoffee.co.uk

f @mumblescoffee 🐦 @mumblescoffee 📷 @mumblescoffee

MAP № 7 SQUARE PEG

29b Gower Road, Sketty, Swansea, SA2 9BX

Square Peg has been a pillar of the Sketty community for over half a decade and continues to fuel locals with quality coffee while simultaneously giving back via charitable projects.

Every surplus penny made at this not-for-profit set-up is donated to local homeless charity Zac's Place, and the perfectly pulled Clifton flat whites taste even sweeter when you know your caffeine habits are supporting a worthy project.

TIP A FEW OF THE LOCALS HAVE BEEN IMMORTALISED ON THE MENU – ASK FOR A 'SHARON' OR A 'DANI'

Also in the spirit of generosity and goodwill, the talented baristas put their years of experience to good use at Square Peg's regular training sessions for coffee freshers eager to learn the craft. The range of SCA-accredited courses covers everything from barista basics to professional skills.

If you're happy to let the team do their thing, give 'em free rein and let them choose your coffee order from the latest guests (regulars include Red Bank, Obadiah and Friedhats). On the food front, new chef Greg Sandles' gratifyingly good specials are a must-order.

ESTABLISHED
2015

KEY ROASTER
Clifton Coffee Roasters

BREWING METHOD
Espresso, batch brew, pourover

MACHINE
La Marzocco Linea PB

GRINDER
Mythos One, Mahlkonig EK43

OPENING HOURS
Mon-Fri 8am-5.30pm
Sat 8am-4pm

Gluten FREE

BEANS AVAILABLE
INSTORE

WIFI

CYCLE FRIENDLY

OUTDOOR SEATING

DISABLED ACCESS

BRING YOUR OWN CUP

COFFEE COURSES

DOG FRIENDLY

---

www.squarepeg.org.uk   T: 01792 206593

f @squarepegcoffee   🐦 @squarepegcoffee   📷 @squarepegcoffee

MAP №8 BASEKAMP

The Warehouse, Kings Lane, Swansea, SA1 2AQ

This espresso bar, eatery and coffee school was founded last year as the Swansea HQ of Afan Coffee Co., a speciality roastery born in the heart of the beautiful Afan Forest.

While the spacious renovated warehouse features a bright white, Scandi-style interior, the minimalist decor is counterbalanced by a warm and welcoming atmosphere. The cafe forms part of a pedestrianised regeneration project in the city and sits among new galleries, boutiques, student digs and co-working spaces.

TIP CHECK OUT THE LIMITED EDITION ESPRESSO STOUT – A COLLAB WITH LOCAL BREWERY TOMOS WATKIN

The constantly changing coffee offering includes a minimum of two espressos and two filter options at any time and utilises a full range of brewing methods, as you might expect at a coffee school. With espresso, V60, Kalita, Chemex, batch and cold brew, this is the place to geek out over taste and technique. As a result of such immense choice, the drinks menu is fittingly divided into 'Coffee' and 'Not Coffee'.

The quality edibles are also a cut above, with regular kitchen takeovers from street food pop-ups a highlight.

ESTABLISHED
2019

KEY ROASTER
Afan Coffee Co.

BREWING METHOD
Espresso, V60,
Kalita Wave,
Chemex,
batch brew,
cold brew

MACHINE
Conti Monte
Carlo

GRINDER
Mahlkonig EK43

OPENING HOURS
Mon-Fri **8.30**am-**5**pm
Sat-Sun **10**am-**5**pm

---

www.basekamp.co.uk   T: 01639 491190

f @basekampswansea   🐦 @basekampswansea   📷 @basekampswansea

HERE TO HELP YOU GROW

Olam
Specialty
Coffee

Tel: +44 (0) 151 498 6500
Email: osceurope@olamnet.com
olamspecialtycoffee.com

MAP №9 96 DEGREES SPECIALITY COFFEE

Unit 7c, Old Masons Yard, Willow Walk, Cowbridge, Glamorgan, CF71 7EE

When Lee Davies and John Howe started making plans for their Cowbridge coffee shop, they knew they wanted to create a space that not only championed speciality coffee but also encouraged social interaction.

So everything at 96 Degrees has been designed to make chatting with chums or striking up a conversation with a stranger easy: sofas ensure extended catch-ups are seriously comfy; table service allows discussions to flow from the get-go; and a #cuppaforamukka board means you can buy forward a coffee.

TIP TALK ABOUT SPREADING THE LOVE – EVERY 50TH TRANSACTION AT THE TILL IS FREE

The caffeine fuelling the chatter is sourced from Bristol speciality pioneers Clifton Coffee. Comforting espresso-based brews lavished with creamy steamed milk are popular, but there's also a hefty selection of filter kit if you're keen to try the latest guest roast.

Decadent homemade cakes and fresh-from-the-griddle toasties fortify the offering if you're in it for the long haul. And, if you drop by from 3pm on a Friday or Saturday, you'll find cocktails, craft beer and wine lubricating the conversations.

ESTABLISHED
2019

KEY ROASTER
Clifton Coffee Roasters

BREWING METHOD
Espresso, V60, Clever Dripper, Chemex

MACHINE
Victoria Arduino Black Eagle

GRINDER
Mythos One, Mahlkonig EK43

OPENING HOURS
Mon-Thu 8am-5pm
Fri 8am-11pm
Sat 9am-11pm
Sun 9.30am-2.30pm

 Gluten FREE

 BEANS AVAILABLE INSTORE

 WIFI

 CYCLE FRIENDLY

 OUTDOOR seating

 DISABLED ACCESS

 BRING YOUR OWN Cup

www.96degreescoffee.co.uk   T: 07876 350684

f @96degreescoffee   🐦 @96degreescoffee   📷 @96_degreescoffee

MAP №10 BLANCHE BAKERY

16 Mackintosh Place, Roath, Cardiff, CF24 4RQ

'**B**ut first coffee'. That's the mantra at Cardiff's pioneering vegan coffee shop and bakery, and it's emblazoned in hot-pink neon bulbs on its lush living wall.

Clearly Blanche is one of the capital's most Instagrammable spots for a latte and, happily, the tiny cafe's photo-ready interior is more than matched by a food and drink menu that deserves its own moment in the limelight.

TIP THE TEAM ARE FLUID WITH THEIR ROASTERS; TRY SOMETHING NEW ON EACH VISIT

Word of mouth is strong at BB and it's steadily grown a fanbase of dedicated regulars and keen visitors since opening in December 2017. It's easy to see – and taste – why, as founders Amy and Rem individually dose every shot to maximise consistency and reduce waste, using beans from roasters such as Round Hill, Assembly, Dark Arts and Neighbourhood.

You're guaranteed a killer flat white here, not to mention an insanely good french-toast doughnut to see you through until lunch. Sticking around? The epic Korean tofu burger and a cold brew tonic is a good call.

ESTABLISHED
2017

KEY ROASTER
Multiple roasters

BREWING METHOD
Espresso, batch brew, AeroPress, drip

MACHINE
Kees van der Westen

GRINDER
Mahlkonig EK43

OPENING HOURS
Mon-Tue, Thu-Sat
11am-**6**pm
Sun **11**am-**4**pm

BEANS AVAILABLE

INSTORE

WIFI

BRING YOUR OWN Cup.

---

www.blanchebakery.co.uk

f @blanchecardiff 🐦 @blanchebakery 📷 @blanche.bakery

11 BRODIES COFFEE CO

Gorsedd Gardens, Cardiff, CF10 3NP

F eel the need to escape the hubbub of Cardiff city centre? Take a two-minute stroll from busy Queen Street and find yourself in the calming oasis of caffeine and greenery that is Gorsedd Gardens.

Follow the stream of flagging visitors and frazzled workers to the old park-keeper's hut to discover Ian Brodie slinging flat whites and long blacks on his trusty La Marzocco. Then all you need do is join the crowd savouring take-out brews on the cluster of alfresco seats – maybe adding a chunky slab of traybake to your order if a little self care is required.

TIP LEAVE YOUR PENNIES AT HOME: BRODIES HAS GONE CASH-FREE

In summer, regulars swap Black Gold espresso-based drinks for bottles of refreshing "coal brew" which is also crafted from beans roasted by Coaltown in the Amman Valley. Other sunshine specials include colourful zero-caffeine turmeric and beetroot lattes.

It's not just the quality coffee and leafy setting that are garnering good vibes at Brodies: Ian recently launched a hot-drinks-for-the-homeless programme in response to the growing number of people sleeping on the streets in Cardiff.

ESTABLISHED
2016

KEY ROASTER
Coaltown Coffee Roasters

BREWING METHOD
Espresso, cold brew, batch brew

MACHINE
La Marzocco Linea PB

GRINDER
Mythos One

OPENING HOURS
Mon-Fri **8**am-**5**pm
Sat-Sun **10**am-**5**pm

 Gluten FREE

 BEANS AVAILABLE INSTORE

 CYCLE FRIENDLY

 OUTDOOR SEATING

 DISABLED ACCESS

 BRING YOUR OWN CUP

 DOG FRIENDLY

T: 07414 963591

f @brodiescoffee @brodiescoffee @brodies_coffee

12 SECRET GARDEN CAFE

Bute Park, North Road, Cardiff, CF10 3ER

The leafy oasis of Bute Park provides a rejuvenating hit of greenery and fresh air in Cardiff's concrete city centre, so it's fitting that the cafe at its heart is a champion for sustainability.

The eco-minded crew at Penylan Pantry took over the walled-garden coffee shop in 2018 and have worked consistently to reduce its environmental impact: rooftop solar panels, fully compostable take-out ware and a no-messing attitude to waste are all new additions.

TIP POOCHES AREN'T JUST WELCOME, THEY'RE ACTIVELY ENCOURAGED

Ingredients for the veg-centric menu of brunches, light lunches and cakes are mostly sourced from local producers (some items are even grown in the park), while a number of the seasonal coffees are roasted in Cardiff. Local roasteries Hard Lines and Lufkin take turns with northern Hasbean in the bean line-up.

When the sun's shining, join the queue of dog walkers and day-trippers eagerly anticipating an affogato made with vegan soft serve and silky espresso. But if you can't bag a seat under the alfresco canopy, grab a flat white to-go from the takeaway hatch and head off on a riverside ramble along the Taff Trail.

ESTABLISHED
2018

KEY ROASTER
Hasbean

BREWING METHOD
Espresso,
batch brew

MACHINE
Nuova Simonelli
Aurelia II

GRINDER
Nuova Simonelli
Mythos One

OPENING HOURS
Mon-Sun 10am-5pm
(reduced in winter)

Gluten FREE

CYCLE FRIENDLY

OUTDOOR SEATING

DISABLED ACCESS

BRING YOUR OWN Cup

DOG FRIENDLY

---

www.secretgardencafecardiff.wordpress.com   T: 02921 321800

@secretgardencf   @secretgardencf

MAP№ 13 KIN + ILK – PONTCANNA

31 Cathedral Road, Pontcanna, Cardiff, CF11 9HB

A short stroll from the tree-fringed banks of the River Taff, the original KIN + ILK café (there are now a couple in the city centre, too) is worth tracking down for its warm-and-welcoming neighbourhood vibes.

Inside, utility-modern design encourages visitors to linger over their chosen brew, while outside tables invite revellers to enjoy their pick of the drinks list alfresco.

Coffee is serious business for the KIN + ILK crew. They're on first-name terms with the El Salvadorian farmer who grows the beans for their house espresso and have maintained a fruitful relationship with him for a couple of years. It's a three-way ménage that also involves the Clifton Coffee team, who take care of the Finca El Corozo roast.

SHORT TIP SANDWICHES FROM THE GRAB-AND-GO RANGE COME IN COMPOSTABLE VEGWARE PACKAGING

To make the most of the experience you'll also need to try out the edibles: quality local ingredients including artisan breads and Welsh cheeses are imaginatively paired and exotically spiced. We'd recommend easing into the day with a brunch of Eggs Salvador, where smoky beans and jalapeño peppers mingle with deliciously runny yolks.

ESTABLISHED
2016

KEY ROASTER
Clifton Coffee Roasters

BREWING METHOD
Espresso, V60, batch brew

MACHINE
La Marzocco Linea PB

GRINDER
Mythos One x 3, Mahlkonig

OPENING HOURS
Mon-Fri **7.30**am-**6**pm
Sat-Sun **9**am-**5**pm

Gluten FREE

BEANS AVAILABLE
INSTORE

WiFi

CYCLE FRIENDLY

OUTDOOR seating

DISABLED ACCESS

BRING YOUR OWN cup

COFFEE COURSES

DOG FRIENDLY

www.kinandilk.com T: 02920 789842

@kinandilk

№14 CORNER COFFEE

13 High Street, Cardiff, CF10 1AX

It was time spent at Bristol indies Small Street Espresso and Society Cafe that inspired Laura McDonald and Cary Frame to plunge into a new career, cross the Severn Bridge and take over Cardiff's Corner Coffee in 2019.

Keen to keep the cafe's loyal following sweet, the couple haven't changed the winning formula too much. While the house coffee has recently been switched to Triple Co, the brews are crafted by the original team of enthusiastic baristas who know how to sling a mean espresso. Guests feature the likes of The Missing Bean, Origin and Campbell & Syme.

TIP A CROWD-PLEASING ALL-DAY BRUNCH MENU RUNS THROUGHOUT THE WEEK

Five coffee options are available in total, including two espressos, two filters and a batch and, whether you go down the flat white or pourover route, a side order of homemade triple-choc brownie is always a good idea.

Corner Coffee marries a love of quality coffee with a passion for the slopes: check out the unique boarding-meets-coffee mural on the wall.

ESTABLISHED
2017

KEY ROASTER
Triple Co Roast

BREWING METHOD
Espresso, V60, batch brew, cold brew

MACHINE
Faema E71

GRINDER
Mahlkonig Twin Air

OPENING HOURS
Mon-Fri 8am-6pm
Sat 8.30am-6pm
Sun 10am-5pm

T: 02921 320400

@cornercoffee_co

MAP 15 KIN + ILK – THE HAYES

1a Hill Street, The Hayes, Cardiff, CF10 2LE

Thanks to the opening of this third branch of KIN + ILK, Cardiff's caffeine lovers can now officially consider themselves spoilt for choice. This time, the speciality-coffee gurus have landed at The Hayes.

The well-tested KIN + ILK approach prevails and pared-back interior design lets the beans take the limelight. Opt for the house fave, Finca El Corozo, to taste the fruits of El Salvadorian grower Fernando Lima's work. Fernando farms in volcanic soils on the slopes of Ilamatepec and has enjoyed a successful long-time collaboration with KIN + ILK and its roaster Clifton Coffee.

OWNERS TIP THIS KIN+ILK OUTPOST WAS NAMED AS ONE OF THE BEST POP-UPS IN THE UK

In addition to espresso classics from the Modbar machine, visitors can also opt for V60 or batch filter. To switch things up, choose one of the guest grinds from Square Mile or The Barn and add a squishy Chocolate Brownie Company bake for a hard-to-beat combo.

For more substantial sustenance, turn to the popular brekkie, brunch and lunch menus. Welsh ingredients are prioritised and crafted into hearty and imaginative plates. Caerphilly cheese sourdough toastie with spiced carrot chutney? Oh, yes.

ESTABLISHED
2020

KEY ROASTER
Clifton Coffee
Roasters

BREWING METHOD
Espresso, V60,
batch brew

MACHINE
Modbar

GRINDER
Mythos One,
Mythos 2,
Mahlkonig EK43

OPENING HOURS
Mon-Fri 7.30am-8pm
Sat 8am-7pm
Sun 9am-5pm

 Gluten FREE

 BEANS AVAILABLE INSTORE

 WIFI

 OUTDOOR SEATING

 DISABLED ACCESS

 BRING YOUR OWN CUP

COFFEE COURSES

DOG FRIENDLY

www.kinandilk.com T: 02920 789842

@kinandilk

ᴹᴬᴾ№ 16 THE PLAN

28-29 Morgan Arcade, Cardiff, CF10 1AF

Sucker for unique coffee shops and Victorian architecture? You'll want to pin this central Cardiff cafe on your Google Maps.

The Plan bucks the trend for industrial minimalism and instead basks in its glass-encased setting at the heart of Morgan Arcade. The almost hexagonal space is set over two floors, with a mezzanine level encircling the solid wood bar at which experienced head barista Trevor Hyam crafts coffee using beans from Herefordshire roastery James Gourmet.

INSIDER'S TIP
UKBC FINALIST TREVOR IS ALWAYS HAPPY TO CHAT COFFEE – ASK HIM FOR HIS PICK OF THE DAY

Table service encourages visitors to unwind and take time over their coffee, so treat yourself to an hour out to browse the current bean selection, order a french press and then sip in quiet contemplation as busy shoppers scuttle past the floor-to-ceiling windows.

If a slice of locally baked cake rouses your appetite, you'll find lots of delicious and sustaining choices on the all-day menu of breakfast-through-to-lunch delights.

ESTABLISHED
2002

KEY ROASTER
James Gourmet Coffee

BREWING METHOD
Espresso, french press, batch brew, cold brew

MACHINE
Astoria Plus 4 You

GRINDER
Anfim Super Caimano

OPENING HOURS
Mon-Sat **8.45**am-**5**pm
Sun **10**am-**4**pm

Gluten FREE

BEANS AVAILABLE INSTORE

WIFI

OUTDOOR SEATING

---

www.theplancafecardiff.co.uk   T: 02920 398764

f @theplancafecardiff   🐦 @theplancafe   📷 @theplancafe

MAP № 17 UNCOMMON GROUND COFFEE ROASTERY

10-12 Royal Arcade, Cardiff, CF10 1AE

S ince it was founded in 2015 by bean-loving brothers Paul and Ian Hayman, Uncommon Ground has become one of the city's coffee institutions.

The siblings split their time between the Uncommon Ground roastery and the city centre cafe, bringing their passion for quality and great service to everything – from bronzing the beans to taking orders and slinging shots at the La Spaziale machine.

INSIDER'S TIP HEAD OVER EARLY TO START YOUR DAY WITH A HEARTY BREAKFAST BURRITO

This level of dedication has resulted in some cracking coffees, including the Original Uncommon Ground Espresso which has been perfected over half a decade. The sweet and lively blend is as good served black as it is adorned with gently steamed milk, and a selection of house-roasted single origins get the same level of love.

In its prime spot in Royal Arcade, the cafe feels more like a cool bar thanks to its atmospheric lighting, quirky design pieces and sociable ambience. Unsurprisingly, it's a fave location for laptop tappers and shoppers who visit to refuel with a fragrant brew and pick of the snack, sandwich and cake menu.

ESTABLISHED
2015

KEY ROASTER
Uncommon Ground

BREWING METHOD
Espresso, V60, batch brew, AeroPress, cold brew

MACHINE
La Spaziale

GRINDER
Anfim x 2, Mazzer Super Jolly

OPENING HOURS
Mon-Sat 7.30am-6.30pm
Sun 10am-5.30pm

 Gluten FREE

 BEANS AVAILABLE INSTORE

 WIFI

 CYCLE FRIENDLY

 OUTDOOR SEATING

 BRING YOUR OWN CUP

COFFEE COURSES

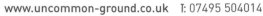

www.uncommon-ground.co.uk   T: 07495 504014

f @uncommongroundcoffeeroastery   🐦 @_uncommonground   📷 @_uncommonground

MAP№18 LUFKIN COFFEE ROASTERS

183-185 Clare Road, Grangetown, Cardiff, CF11 6QS

From its original Pontcanna base, Lufkin has sprouted a number of offshoots and this, the largest of the trio, is the new heart of the speciality operation.

Founders Dan and Frances have brought their American roots to Grangetown and given a former bank the full Cali treatment. They've installed roomy communal tables as well as an open-plan bar to remove the barrier between barista and coffee drinker. The focus on filter and a counter of fresh-from-the-oven pies provide further stateside references.

The coffee is roasted in what was once the bank's vault, and then served as espresso, batch brew and pourovers in locally made hand-thrown ceramic cups. If you're inspired by the gorgeous ceramics, join one of the clay classes held weekly in the cafe.

TIP CHECK OUT THE OTHER LUFKIN VENUES IN PONTCANNA AND THOMPSON'S PARK

Thanks to the classes (and other events such as regular food pop-ups from West Pizza, coffee workshops and weekend yoga sessions) Lufkin has become a community hub. And what's better after a stretch session than coffee and a slice of pie?

ESTABLISHED
2019

KEY ROASTER
Lufkin Coffee Roasters

BREWING METHOD
Espresso, pourover, batch brew

MACHINE
La Marzocco Linea PB

GRINDER
Victoria Arduino Mythos One

OPENING HOURS
Mon-Sun
9.30am-3.30pm

BEANS AVAILABLE INSTORE

WIFI

CYCLE FRIENDLY

DISABLED ACCESS

BRING YOUR OWN Cup

COFFEE COURSES

DOG FRIENDLY

---

www.lufkincoffee.com   T: 07570 811763

f @lufkincoffee   🐦 @lufkincoffee   📷 @lufkincoffee

MAP№ 19 QUANTUM COFFEE ROASTERS

58 Bute Street, Butetown, Cardiff, CF10 5BN

Day-trippers who take the circular route from Cardiff Bay over the Barrage to Penarth are rewarded on return with own-roasted coffee and chubby slices of traybake at this quayside favourite.

The coffee shop is set back from the throng of chain restaurants and cafes which overlook the water, so it's a great place to escape the crowds while sinking a decent cup. It's spacious too and, even if the line of eager customers is almost to the door, you'll usually find a couple of armchairs going spare.

TIP WANT TO TRY A FLAT WHITE MARTINI? DROP IN DURING ONE OF THE LIVE MUSIC EVENTS

Beans used in the orchestra of grinders and filter kit are bronzed in the city at Quantum's roastery HQ. There's a huge selection of coffees to choose from, including a new collection of Wales-inspired blends, plus Greek-style coffees which pay homage to founders Katia and Dimitri's heritage.

This year the team have made a quantum leap into tea blending, so the cafe also offers an extensive range of loose-leaf infusions.

ESTABLISHED
2015

KEY ROASTER
Quantum Coffee Roasters

BREWING METHOD
Espresso, V60, nitro, ibrik, Chemex

MACHINE
La Marzocco Linea 3AV

GRINDER
Santos, Mazzer, Zaras

OPENING HOURS
Mon-Fri 8am-6pm
Sat 9am-6pm
Sun 10am-6pm
(extended in summer)

---

www.quantumroasters.co.uk   T: 07413 543335

f @quantumroasters   🐦 @quantumroasters   📷 @quantumroasters

MAP №20 QUARTERS COFFEE

Glen Avon House, Millennium Walk, Newport, NP19 0LZ

For a busy city, Newport is somewhat lacking in speciality coffee shops. Cross the river from the built-up centre, however, and you'll find the team at Quarters working hard to fill the gap.

Founders Jon and Jack set out to create a warm and welcoming space on the banks of the Usk where the local community could gather to work and catch up with friends over great coffee. *'We wanted our space to feel like an extension of our guests' living quarters – hence the name,'* says Jon.

This riverside spot has become a firm favourite among locals, freelancers, families and cyclists, and the team work closely alongside North Star in Leeds to provide a coffee line-up on espresso and filter which is not only delicious but also sourced with sustainability in mind.

TIP MAKE THE MOST OF THE FREELANCER DEAL – UNLIMITED HOT DRINKS EACH DAY FOR £7.50

The North Star team can often be found at Quarters running public cuppings, workshops and ongoing SCA training with the baristas.

ESTABLISHED
2018

KEY ROASTER
North Star
Coffee Roasters

BREWING METHOD
Espresso, V60,
batch brew

MACHINE
La Marzocco
Linea PB ABR

GRINDER
Fiorenzato F64,
Mahlkonig EK43

OPENING HOURS
Mon-Fri 8am-6pm
Sat 9am-6pm

www.quarterscoffee.com   T: 07920 037837

f @quarterscoffee   🐦 @quarterscoffee   📷 @quarterscoffee

ᴹᴬᴾ№21 BEAN & BREAD

36 Lion Street, Abergavenny, Monmouthshire, NP7 5PE

The plant-based movement continues to gather momentum and this Monmouthshire coffee shop is a fine example of the contemporary flexitarian approach to food and drink.

A whopping 80 per cent of the menu is vegan, so veg-centric visitors have plenty of choice, while those with broader eating habits still get to incorporate eggs and smoked salmon into their weekend.

ᴵᴺˢᴵᴰᴱᴿˢTIP IT'S 5PM SOMEWHERE; ADD AN ESPRESSO-BASED COCKTAIL OR GLASS OF VEGAN WINE TO YOUR ORDER

If you're not doing dairy, you'll find a selection of alt milks to pair with Coaltown's Black Gold No 3 coffee blend. Or simply go black, courtesy of a monthly changing pourover from the South Wales roastery. Speciality drinks include turmeric, matcha and beetroot lattes, while freshly blitzed smoothies further fortify the liquid offering.

Founder Jessica Fletcher was inspired to open a place of her own after living in New Zealand, and antipodean creativity runs through both the speciality coffee and slick interior decor. Grab a spot on the long communal table or settle down in one of the Scandi-style armchairs and drink in the good vibes.

ESTABLISHED
2018

KEY ROASTER
Coaltown Coffee Roasters

BREWING METHOD
Espresso, pourover

MACHINE
La Marzocco

GRINDER
Victoria Arduino Mythos One

OPENING HOURS
Tue-Fri 9am-5pm
Sat-Sun 10am-4pm

---

www.beanandbread.co.uk   T: 07954 131995
f @beanandbreadwales   🐦 @beanandbread_   📷 @beanandbread_

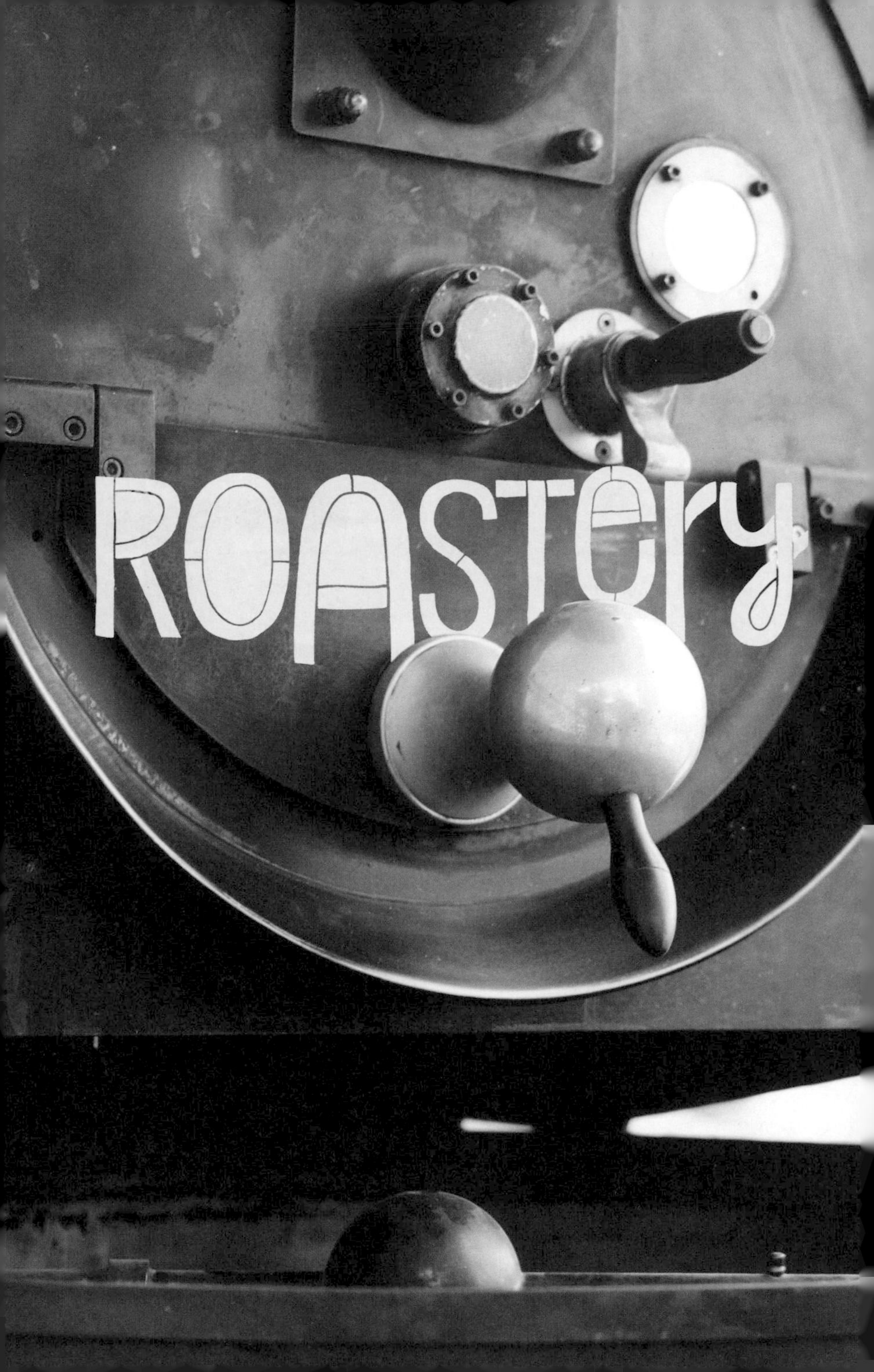
ROASTERY

MAP N°22 AFAN COFFEE CO.

Ground Floor, The Warehouse, Kings Lane, Swansea, SA1 2AQ

At this family-founded roastery, great things are taking place in the quest to unlock the flavour potential of each green bean which ends up in the Portuguese cast-iron Joper. The Afan team champion ethical trading and seasonality and source a smorgasbord of micro-lots and single origins.

Planet-friendly practices are prioritised and, after roasting, coffee makes the journey to local wholesalers in reusable and returnable airtight drums. A recent collab with local brewery Tomos Watkins has also seen spent coffee pucks metamorphosed into a limited edition coffee stout.

'FROM THE AFAN FOREST TO AN ULTRA-MODERN URBAN ROASTERY'

A recent move from the Afan Forest to an ultra-modern urban roastery space in Swansea city centre has enabled the crew to introduce a training school and also give coffee fans the chance to sample Afan brews at BASEKAMP coffee bar.

ESTABLISHED
2018

ROASTER
MAKE & SIZE
Joper 5kg

CAFE ONSITE

OPEN BY APPOINTMENT

COFFEE COURSES

BEANS AVAILABLE
ONLINE ONSITE

www.afancoffee.co.uk   T: 01639 491190

f @afancoffeeco   🐦 @affancoffee   📷 @afancoffee

GLOUCESTERSHIRE& OXFORDSHIRE&

№25

Ue Coffee Roastery Cafe And Kitchen

ILTER BREW

O	£3.50
ROPRESS	£3.50
EMEX	£3.50

L DRINKS AVAILABLE TO GO WITH
OP REDUCTION IN PRICE.

UR BARISTA WILL BE ONLY TOO
PPY TO INTRODUCE YOU TO OUR
EST COFFEE OF THE MONTH, IN
TH ESPRESSO AND FILTER

TEA

BREAKFAST TEA	£2.80
EARL OF GREY	£2.80
GIRLIE GREY	£2.80
WINTER BREW	£2.80
DRAGONWELL GREEN	£2.80
IRON BUDDA OOLONG	£3.00
MOJITO MINT	£2.80
SPICED APPLE CIDER	£2.80
MATCHA FLAT WHITE	£3.20
TURMERIC FLAT WHITE	£3.00
SPICED MASALA CHAI LATTE	£3.00

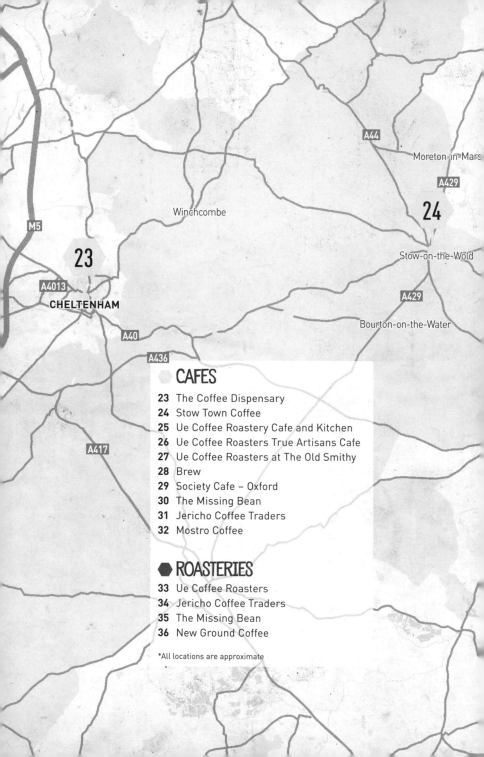

CHELTENHAM

Winchcombe

Moreton-in-Mars

Stow-on-the-Wold

Bourton-on-the-Water

M5
A44
A429
A4013
A40
A436
A417

23

24

CAFES

ROASTERIES

*All locations are approximate

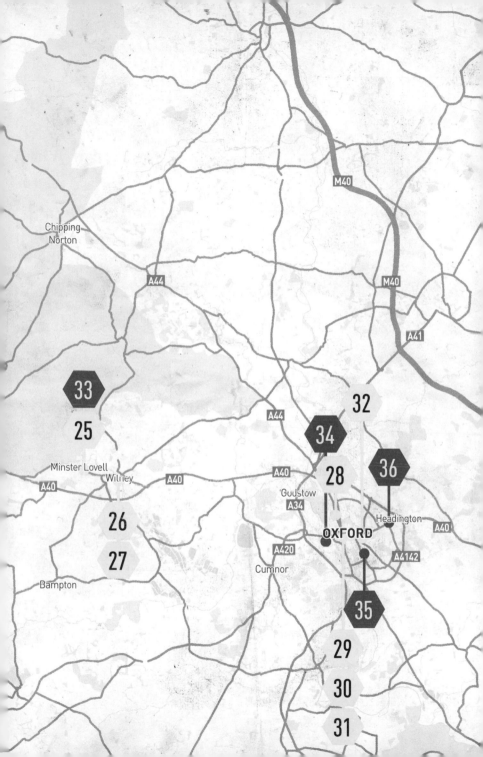

MAP №23 THE COFFEE DISPENSARY

18 Regent Street, Cheltenham, Gloucestershire, GL50 1HE

This former pharmacy plays a vital role in the daily routines of Cheltenham locals who like to take a regular dose of top-grade caffeine.

Its band of knowledgeable baristas have been dispensing coffee since 2015 and are thoroughly proficient in prescribing the perfect brew – whatever the tastes and requirements of the customer. Need a quick fix? Make it a batch brew to-go. Got time to linger over something more complex? Let the team recommend one of the new fermentation-processed single origins. Craving the fuss-free familiarity of a well-made flat white? They're a dab hand at those, too.

☞TIP AFTER-HOURS EVENTS INCLUDE BREWING WORKSHOPS AND LIVE MUSIC

While the expansive range of guest coffees is worth perusing (regular appearances include Quarter Horse, Colonna and Clifton), The Coffee Dispensary is one of the first venues in the country to use beans from Fire & Flow. The new roastery – headed up by *Indy Coffee Guide* committee member and UKBC regular Callum Parsons – launched in the Cotswolds late last year, so don't miss the opportunity to sample locally roasted beans and be in on the hot new thing.

ESTABLISHED
2015

KEY ROASTER
Fire & Flow
Coffee Roasters

BREWING METHOD
Espresso,
pourover, batch
brew, cold drip

MACHINE
Sanremo Opera

GRINDER
Victoria Arduino
Mythos 2,
Mahlkonig EK43

OPENING HOURS
Mon-Tue **8.30**am-**5**pm
Wed-Fri **8.30**am-**5.30**pm
Sat **9**am-**5.30**pm
Sun **10**am-**4.30**pm

 Gluten FREE

 BEANS AVAILABLE INSTORE

 WIFI

 CYCLE FRIENDLY

 OUTDOOR SEATING

 BRING YOUR OWN Cup.

 COFFEE COURSES

 DOG FRIENDLY

---

www.the-coffee-dispensary.co.uk   **T:** 01242 260597

f @thecoffeedispensary15   🐦 @coffeedispenser   📷 @the_coffee_dispensary

№ 24 STOW TOWN COFFEE

2 Wells Barn, Sheep Street, Stow-on-the-Wold, Gloucestershire, GL54 1AA

Locals might be reluctant to spill the beans on this little Stow-on-the-Wold roastery, especially its secret imbibing room. Those in the know, however, head upstairs to snatch a clandestine moment with freshly roasted beans in the secluded coffee lounge.

Should the comfy chairs already be occupied, sippers park themselves in the tiny downstairs seating area and watch the bean-bronzing taking place in Gerard the small-batch Toper roaster. Both are cosy spots in which to sample the Colombian-Sumatran house blend as a velvety flat white.

☞ TIP IF THERE'S AN AFTERNOON ROASTING SESSION IN PROCESS, POP IN FOR A TAKE-OUT COFFEE

A small-is-beautiful ethos extends to all aspects of this roastery, and owners David and Alison Cunliffe focus on supplying local businesses within a 20-mile radius. It enables them to maintain close relationships with their customers while also helping deliver on Stow Town's low-carbon goals.

Although not a cafe in the traditional sense, this is a welcoming den for speciality lovers who want to savour a quality sip, buy single origin beans for their home brew bar or even sign up for a coffee course.

ESTABLISHED
2017

KEY ROASTER
Stow Town Coffee

BREWING METHOD
Espresso

MACHINE
Fracino Contempo

GRINDER
Caedo F375

OPENING HOURS
Mon-Fri **8**am-**12**pm

BEANS AVAILABLE
INSTORE

OUTDOOR SEATING

DISABLED ACCESS

COFFEE COURSES

DOG FRIENDLY

www.stowtowncoffee.co.uk　T: 01451 832519

f @stowtowncoffee　◎ @stowtowncoffee

MAP 25 UE COFFEE ROASTERY CAFE AND KITCHEN

11a Windrush Industrial Park, Linkwood Road, Witney, Oxfordshire, OX29 7HA

As most speciality coffee venues tend to be right in the city centre – making a drive-by fix a no-no – it's good to have a pit stop with on-site parking up your sleeve.

The team at Ue have roasted beans at this quiet spot on the Cotswolds-Oxfordshire border since 2009 and, eager to let fellow coffee lovers in on the action, added a cafe and kitchen to their HQ in 2016.

TIP SKIPPED BREAKFAST? ORDER THE TOASTED BANANA BREAD WITH GREEK YOGURT AND HONEY

It's a relaxing space in which to take a couple of hours out to enjoy great coffee and stonking food, and its new gallery area allows visitors to revel in the theatre of a working roastery while sipping the single origin of the month. The team use the UK's first traditional wood-fired coffee roaster, as well as a number of Giesen models, and are always up for a natter about their unique roasting style.

Seasonal and local are the buzzwords at the Kitchen and the menu of wholesome fodder is worth extending any visit to experience: try the sharing shakshuka with hummus, pickles, chillies and flatbread.

ESTABLISHED
2016

KEY ROASTER
Ue Coffee Roasters

BREWING METHOD
Espresso, Chemex, V60, AeroPress

MACHINE
La Marzocco Strada

GRINDER
Mazzer Robur, Mazzer Major, Mahlkonig EK43

OPENING HOURS
Mon-Fri 8.30am-4.30pm
Sat 8.30am-3.30pm

---

www.uecoffeeroasters.com   T: 01993 706767

f @uecoffeeroasterscafes   🐦 @uecoffee   📷 @uecoffeeartisancafes

MAP 26 UE COFFEE ROASTERS TRUE ARTISANS CAFE

62a High Street, Witney, Oxfordshire, OX28 6HJ

Any discerning speciality geek looking to sniff out a true artisan coffee shop serving beans bronzed in-house should make a beeline for Ue.

As the first speciality coffee roastery in Oxfordshire (it blasted onto the bean scene a decade ago), this community of brew buffs has not only brought a superlative speciality experience to the good people of Witney, it has also thoroughly spoilt the town's residents by setting up two individual cafes – plus a brew bar at the roastery.

Another first (and a more recent win) has been the installation of the first La Marzocco Leva 3-group espresso machine to be found in any UK high street cafe.

TIP UE SINGLE ESTATE COFFEES KEEP THE HOUSE ROAST COMPANY

As you may have sussed, innovation and quality are Ue's watchwords, and this also applies to the food. So, when you swing by for your morning AeroPress, it would be a mistake not to hang around to explore the extensive breakfast and brunch menu (toasted banana bread with greek yogurt and honey is the house fave). Alternatively, start your day with a jolt and grab an espresso and homemade bake to-go.

ESTABLISHED
2016

KEY ROASTER
Ue Coffee Roasters

BREWING METHOD
Espresso, filter, V60, Chemex, AeroPress

MACHINE
La Marzocco Leva

GRINDER
Mazzer Robur, Mazzer Kony, Mahlkonig EK43

OPENING HOURS
Mon-Fri **8.30**am-**4.30**pm
Sat **8.30**am-**5**pm
Sun **10**am-**3.30**pm

 Gluten FREE

 BEANS AVAILABLE INSTORE

 WIFI

 OUTDOOR SEATING

 DISABLED ACCESS

 BRING YOUR OWN CUP

 COFFEE COURSES

 DOG FRIENDLY

---

www.uecoffeeroasters.com   T: 01993 706767

f @uecoffeeroasterscafes   🐦 @uecoffee   📷 @uecoffeeartisancafes

№27 UE COFFEE ROASTERS AT THE OLD SMITHY

47 Market Square, Witney, Oxfordshire, OX28 6AG

Ue's hip aesthetic and forward-thinking ethos make a pleasing counterpoint to the traditional setting of Witney's 300-year-old former blacksmiths.

Swing by the smallest outpost of the Ue family to experience own-roasted coffee served as espresso drinks. The house roast is always supplemented by an additional Ue single origin and both are fabulous when imbibed with homebaked carby treats.

The coffee beans travel a short distance from the Linkwood Road roastery to be pulled through the La Marzocco by a group of chirpy baristas. The team pride themselves on knowing their locals' orders and making this speciality swing-by a highlight of their customers' days.

TiP HAND-BLENDED ARTISAN TEAS ARE SUPPLIED BY SISTER COMPANY JEEVES & JERICHO

Just as authentic and carefully crafted as the coffee is the decor and signage: the reclaimed lighting feature that runs through the cafe comes from a salvaged 1970s Japanese submarine.

ESTABLISHED
2016

KEY ROASTER
Ue Coffee Roasters

BREWING METHOD
Espresso

MACHINE
La Marzocco Linea PB

GRINDER
Mazzer Robur,
Mazzer Kony,
Mahlkonig EK43

OPENING HOURS
Mon-Fri 8.30am-4.30pm
Sat 8.30am-5pm
Sun 10am-3.30pm

www.uecoffeeroasters.com   T: 01993 706767

f @uecoffeeroasterscafes   🐦 @uecoffee   📷 @uecoffeeartisancafes

MAP №28 BREW

75b Banbury Road, Oxford, OX2 6PE

If you're looking for quality caffeine away from the hubbub of central Oxford, wander over to North Parade to find the hidden-away entrance to Brew. You'll know you've got the right spot when you clock the cluster of indie shops, then simply follow the scent of freshly ground beans.

Brew may be small but it's perfectly formed as a result of its local owners Will and Arthur kitting it out with all the essentials. A sleek Elektra Sixties espresso machine crowns the bar, a scattering of tables provides somewhere to perch and sip, and a turntable spins tunes from a selection of old-school vinyl.

TIP CAFFEINE OVERKILL? SWITCH TO THE SQUARE MILE DECAF

Single origin beans are sourced from Round Hill and other leading roasters. After dialling in their espresso and filter offering, the tight-knit team of baristas focus on consistency and pair the seasonal lots with Lancaster's Brades Farm milk. They're also dab hands at pouring Oatly rosettas for plant-based visitors.

While there's no room for an on-site kitchen, Brew's cakes and traybakes are all homemade – early birds can also pick up pastries made by local patisserie Gateau.

ESTABLISHED
2013

KEY ROASTER
Round Hill
Roastery

BREWING METHOD
Espresso, V60

MACHINE
Elektra Sixties

GRINDER
Mahlkonig EK43,
Mazzer Major
Electronic

OPENING HOURS
Mon-Fri 7.30am-5.30pm
Sat-Sun 8.30am-5.30pm

www.brewoxford.co.uk

f @brewoxford   🐦 @brew_oxford   @brewoxford

MAP№ 29 SOCIETY CAFE – OXFORD

12-16 St Michael's Street, Oxford, OX1 2DU

'Keep it sassy' is the life advice inscribed on Society's teal-coloured La Marzocco machine, and that's exactly the attitude the team of badass baristas adopt when it comes to curating their top-notch coffee offering.

A seasonally changing house espresso and three different beans available as V60 means there's always something new and noteworthy to sample at the Oxford branch of this speciality micro-chain.

The creative coffee line-up and dedication to the craft makes the spacious venue (there's more seating tucked away downstairs) a pleasing indie alternative to the nearby multinational coffee shops dishing out lacklustre lattes.

TIP FIND OUT ABOUT THE SKILLS AND HOBBIES OF THE BARISTAS IN THE HOUSE NEWSPAPER

Happily, this light and sociable space attracts more than its fair share of customers, from tourists looking for a caffeine pep-up to laptop-tapping local workers whiling away an hour or two with a pourover to the background whirr of the grinder.

ESTABLISHED
2017

KEY ROASTER
Origin Coffee Roasters

BREWING METHOD
Espresso, V60, AeroPress

MACHINE
La Marzocco Linea PB Gravimetric

GRINDER
Mythos One, Mahlkonig EK43

OPENING HOURS
Mon-Fri 7.30am-6.30pm
Sat 8am-6.30pm
Sun 10am-6pm

Gluten FREE

BEANS AVAILABLE INSTORE

WIFI

CYCLE FRIENDLY

DISABLED ACCESS

BRING YOUR OWN Cup

DOG FRIENDLY

www.society-cafe.com   T: 01865 425750

f @societycafe   🐦 @societycafe   📷 @societycafe

MAP №30 THE MISSING BEAN

14 Turl Street, Oxford, OX1 3DQ

From its hidden-away home amid the winding lanes between Oxford's historic colleges, The Missing Bean has provided lecture wake-me-ups and fuelled espresso-precision concentration for over a decade.

Given its neighbours, it's no surprise that this snug hangout is usually chock-full of lecturers and chatty undergrads, and the coffee crew's decision to do without Wifi makes it the ideal destination for a caffeine jolt on a library break. Funky tunes are usually on full blast, creating a buzzy atmosphere in which to indulge in silky smooth coffee crafted from beans bronzed in TMB's own roastery in the city.

TIP THE PLAYLIST OF THE DAY IS DETERMINED BY THE BARISTA: EXPECT AN ECLECTIC MIX

Friendly and quick service means that even if you're between lectures there's still time to explore two regularly changing single origins, prepped as espresso or batch brew.

Those with more time should add a slice from the cake cabinet to their order, then pull up a pew at the window bar, imbibe the lively atmosphere and discover just what they've been missing.

ESTABLISHED
2009

KEY ROASTER
The Missing Bean

BREWING METHOD
Espresso, batch brew

MACHINE
Faema E71

GRINDER
Anfim Pratica, Anfim SP2, Ditting KR804

OPENING HOURS
Mon-Fri 8am-6pm
Sat 9am-6.30pm
Sun 10am-5.30pm

www.themissingbean.co.uk   T: 01865 794886
f @themissingbean   🐦 @themissingbean   📷 @themissingbean

MAP 31 JERICHO COFFEE TRADERS

105 High Street, Oxford, OX1 4BW

S potting Jericho's trademark illustration of the New Zealand pukeko bird on Oxford's bustling High Street is the sign that you've found caffeinated refuge.

The bird references co-owner James Armitage's hometown and honours the people who died in the 2019 Christchurch shootings.

From dawn 'til dusk, the Jericho team provide much-needed fuel for the students, tourists, workers and families who all pop in to this Oxford favourite for their daily fix.

TIP IN 2018, JERICHO SCOOPED OXFORD FRIENDS OF THE EARTH'S TOP AWARD FOR ACTION ON PLASTIC

Thrift-chic decor sits well with the street's ancient history, and an old-school window bar and squishy leather snug out back provide respectively busy and quieter areas in which to park up with a brew and brownie.

The beans are roasted just out of town at Jericho's roastery where the team bronze interesting lots on a 6kg Genio. Pick from an extensive menu of single origins and multitude of brew methods. And if your curiosity is piqued by the range, visit the coffee bar at the roastery.

ESTABLISHED
2017

KEY ROASTER
Jericho Coffee Traders

BREWING METHOD
Espresso, filter, V60, AeroPress, nitro

MACHINE
Victoria Arduino Gravitech Black Eagle

GRINDER
Victoria Arduino Mythos One x 2, Mahlkonig EK43

OPENING HOURS
Mon-Fri **8**am-**5.30**pm
Sat **8.30**am-**5**pm
Sun **9**am-**5**pm

Gluten FREE

BEANS AVAILABLE INSTORE

BRING YOUR OWN Cup

COFFEE COURSES

DOG FRIENDLY

---

www.jerichocoffeetraders.com T: 07879 400163

f @jerichocoffeetraders 🐦 @jericofftraders 📷 @jerichocoffeetraders

MAP № 32 MOSTRO COFFEE

Truck Store, 101 Cowley Road, Oxford, OX4 1HU

This espresso bar, tucked away in one of Oxford's remaining indie record shops, keeps local music lovers and zapped-of-energy students expertly caffeinated and upbeat, one toe-tapping tune and shot of espresso at a time.

While music pumping from the speakers draws them in, it's the delicious coffee that tempts them to stick around at Mostro. Cornwall's Origin supplies the single origin beans destined for extraction action through the La Marzocco machine, while guest roasters provide funky finds for filter, V60 and AeroPress.

TIP THE BROWNIES ARE THE STUFF OF LEGEND; PICK UP A SLAB WITH YOUR 'SPRO

The retro space hosts live gigs every week and past performers have included the likes of Oxford-formed Foals. The baristas pep up the audience with silky smooth coffee before the tempo is ramped up and the caffeine swapped for craft ale.

Day-tripper? After you've finished vinyl rummaging, pull up a stool at the window and bliss out to the background beats while sipping a speciality-grade brew and tucking in to a warm and sticky cinnamon bun.

ESTABLISHED
2015

KEY ROASTER
Origin Coffee Roasters

BREWING METHOD
Espresso, V60, batch brew, AeroPress

MACHINE
La Marzocco Linea Classic AV

GRINDER
Mythos One, Mahlkonig EK43

OPENING HOURS
Mon-Fri **8.30**am-**6**pm
Sat **10**am-**6.30**pm
Sun **11**am-**5.30**pm

 Gluten FREE

 BEANS AVAILABLE INSTORE

 WiFi

 CYCLE FRIENDLY

 OUTDOOR seating

 DISABLED ACCESS

 BRING YOUR OWN Cup

DOG FRIENDLY

www.truckmusicstore.co.uk   T: 01865 793866
f @mostrocoffeeoxford   @mostrocoffee   @mostrocoffee

ROASTERIES

Nº35
The Missing Bean

MAP 33 UE COFFEE ROASTERS

11a-11b Windrush Industrial Park, Linkwood Road, Witney, Oxfordshire, OX29 7HA

Ever since they lit the first logs in their roaster, the team behind Ue have chosen to do things differently and were the first (and remain the only) indie in the UK to roast on a traditional wood-fired roaster.

While their methods may be rooted in tradition, the team employ bang-up-to-date technology to keep their coffee offering competitive, roasting on a medley of gas-fuelled Giesens (alongside the Coffee-Tech Ghibli) to sustain demand. Ue's lengthy customer list of Michelin starred restaurants, five star hotels and high-end coffee shops attest to the quality-over-quantity approach.

'THE FIRST INDIE IN THE UK TO ROAST ON A WOOD-FIRED ROASTER'

In 2019, the roastery on the Cotswolds-Oxfordshire border celebrated its tenth birthday with the unveiling of a new training school and coffee lab. The on-site cafe and kitchen also received a revamp, and now a fresh gallery area allows curious coffee fans to sip a single origin pourover while they watch the roasters working on the next batch of beans.

ESTABLISHED
2009

ROASTER
MAKE & SIZE
Giesen W30
Giesen W15
Giesen WPG1
Coffee-Tech
Ghibli Firewood

CAFE ONSITE

OPEN TO THE PUBLIC

COFFEE COURSES

COURSES

BEANS AVAILABLE
ONLINE ONSITE

---

www.uecoffeeroasters.com   T: 01993 706767

f @uecoffeeroasters   🐦 @uecoffee   @uecoffeeroasters

MAP № 34 JERICHO COFFEE TRADERS

Unit 2, Roger House, Osney Mead, Oxford, OX2 0ES

A short wander along the canal from central Oxford leads to an unassuming roastery-cafe which bubbles with energy and character.

Proud Kiwi James Armitage and wife Lizzie (an even prouder Devonian) are the friendly duo heading up Jericho Coffee Traders. Their long-held dream of working in speciality came to fruition in 2009 when they spotted a three-wheeled Vespa Piaggio Ape for sale by the side of the road. They snapped it up and, after fitting a coffee machine in the back, joined the Oxford coffee community by selling NZ-standard flat whites from Magdalen Bridge.

'ROASTERY-CAFE WHICH BUBBLES WITH ENERGY'

As demand for their brews grew and an opportunity arose to open a cafe on Oxford High Street, James and Lizzie decided to take more control over what they were serving and began roasting ethically procured greens. Now, in addition to supplying their own busy coffee shops and wholesale partners, JCT ships beans worldwide to a legion of subscribers.

ESTABLISHED
2015

ROASTER
MAKE & SIZE
Genio 6kg
North 3kg

CAFE ONSITE

OPEN BY APPOINTMENT

COFFEE COURSES

BEANS AVAILABLE
ONLINE ONSITE

www.jerichocoffeetraders.com   T: 07879 400163
f @jerichocoffeetraders   🐦 @jericofftraders   📷 @jerichocoffeetraders

MAP 35 THE MISSING BEAN

Unit 1, Newtec Place, Magdalen Road, Oxford, OX4 1RE

It was while working part time as a barista in Sydney that Ori Halup (who was studying film at the time) caught the speciality coffee bug. However, it was only on moving to Oxford with his then partner, now business partner, Vicky, and finding nowhere to get a good flat white fix that he seized the opportunity to create the city's first independent speciality coffee shop.

Three years after launching his Turl Street cafe, Ori turned to roasting. At first he only stocked his own coffee shop's grinders, but was soon fuelling a troupe of other cafes in the area. Now, with nearly ten years' coffee experience under their belts, Ori and the team continue to experiment and love nothing more than unlocking funky and complex flavours from beans sourced from growing hotspots around the world.

'UNLOCKING FUNKY AND COMPLEX FLAVOURS'

Their pursuit of top-quality crops has forged five direct-trade relationships, including the most recent partnership with Fincas Mierisch in Nicaragua. The gang visit the farmers at origin whenever they can, taking great pride in seeing the difference their Oxford-roasted coffee has on the farming communities.

ESTABLISHED
2014

ROASTER
MAKE & SIZE
Giesen W15A

Ikawa sample roaster

CAFE ONSITE

OPEN TO THE PUBLIC

COFFEE COURSES

BEANS AVAILABLE
ONLINE ONSITE

---

www.themissingbean.co.uk   T: 01865 236650

f @themissingbean   🐦 @themissingbean   📷 @themissingbean

MAP №36 NEW GROUND COFFEE

Workshop rear of Simon House, 2 Windmill Road, Oxford, OX3 7BU

This Oxford outfit may be a relative newbie on the roasting block, but it's already making great strides on the road to achieving its unique coffee mission.

Owners Dickon and Joel combined their passions for justice and great caffeine in the creation of a social enterprise that provides training and job opportunities for ex-offenders in the Thames Valley.

High-grade greens are ethically sourced from regions including Colombia, Ethiopia, Uganda and Papua New Guinea and bronzed at the roastery on a chunky (and planet friendly) Loring S15 Falcon. The roaster produces consistently good coffees from an ever-changing selection of single origin beans.

'TRAINING AND JOB OPPORTUNITIES FOR EX-OFFENDERS'

An industrial-chic cafe has recently been opened on-site too (there's also a pop-up in Selfridges, London), helping New Ground create a complete, compassionate coffee experience.

ESTABLISHED
2018

ROASTER
MAKE & SIZE
Loring S15
Falcon

CAFE ONSITE

OPEN TO THE PUBLIC

BEANS AVAILABLE

www.newgroundcoffee.com   T: 07968 607958

f @newgroundcoffeesocial   @ @newgroundcoffee

EAST & WEST SUSSEX

BRIGHTON
SEE OVER

CAFES

37 Lindfield Coffee Works
38 Stooge Coffee
39 Urban Ground

ROASTERIES

46 Horsham Coffee Roaster
47 Lindfield Coffee Works
49 Pharmacie Coffee Roasters
50 Cast Iron Coffee Roasters

*All locations are approximate

BRIGHTON

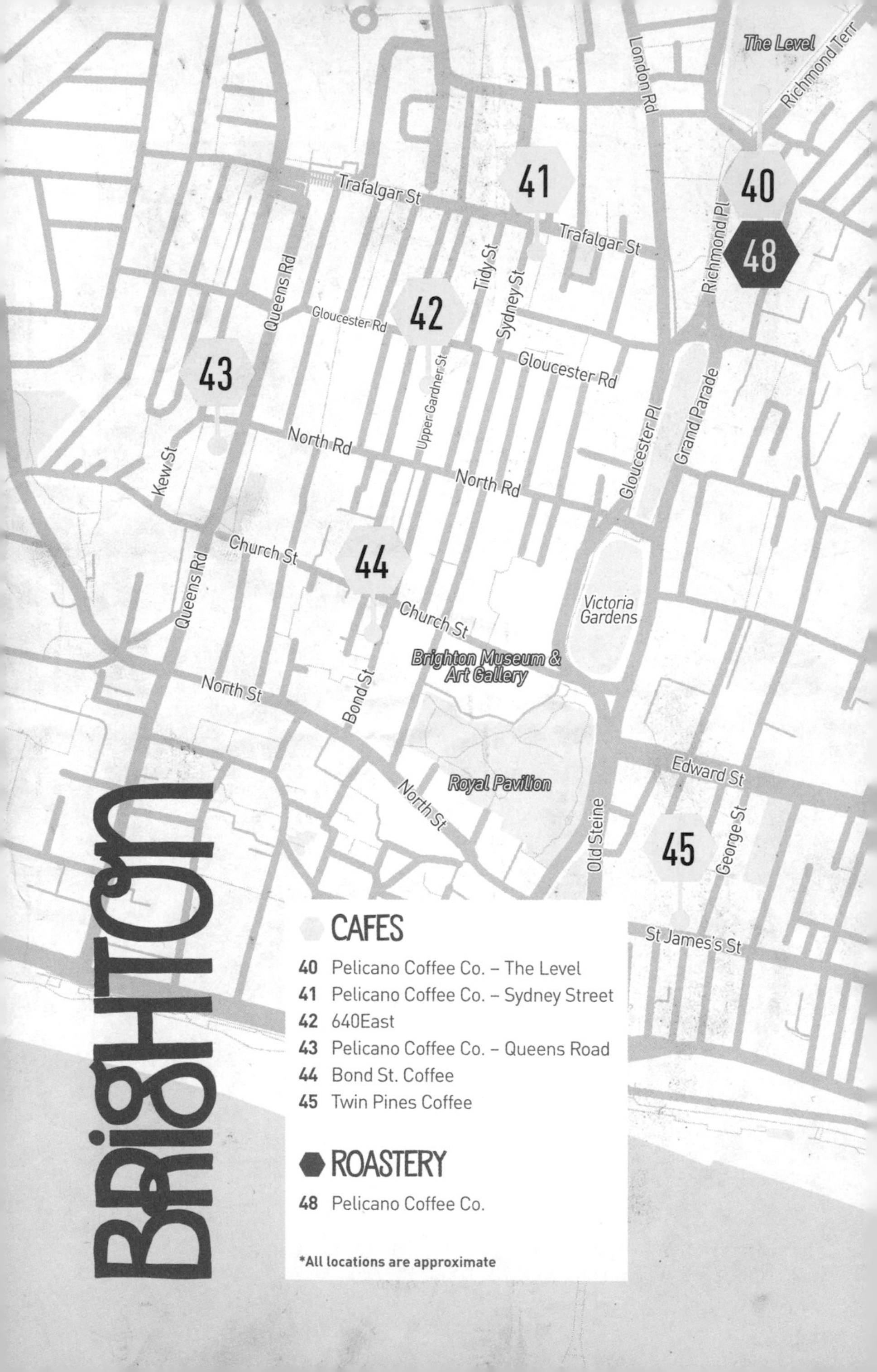
The Level
Richmond Terr
London Rd
Trafalgar St
Trafalgar St
41
40
48
Richmond Pl
Queens Rd
Gloucester Rd
42
Tidy St
Sydney St
Gloucester Rd
43
Upper Gardner St
North Rd
North Rd
Kew St
Gloucester Pl
Grand Parade
Church St
44
Church St
Queens Rd
Victoria Gardens
Brighton Museum & Art Gallery
North St
Bond St
Edward St
Royal Pavilion
North St
Old Steine
45
George St
St James's St

CAFES

40 Pelicano Coffee Co. – The Level
41 Pelicano Coffee Co. – Sydney Street
42 640East
43 Pelicano Coffee Co. – Queens Road
44 Bond St. Coffee
45 Twin Pines Coffee

ROASTERY

48 Pelicano Coffee Co.

***All locations are approximate**

MAP № 37 LINDFIELD COFFEE WORKS

Unit 2, 70 High Street, Lindfield, West Sussex, RH16 2HL

Like to know where the beans used to craft your coffee come from? Then pencil Lindfield into your little book of coffee must-visits as this cool cafe, just off the village High Street, hums with coffee-roasting activity.

Flop down on the leather banquette, order a batch brew and enjoy the waft of gently bronzing beans which make the short journey across the room from roaster to hopper.

The team ethically source greens from a range of origins (40 per cent of the beans are directly imported from three farms in Colombia) so there's usually something new and interesting to sample. Alongside the house blend, a single origin batch changes daily while a second espresso option is updated each month.

TIP CAN'T FIND IT? LEAVE THE HIGH STREET, HEAD DOWN ALMA ROAD AND FOLLOW THE WAFT OF COFFEE

As well as the class coffee, you'll find a kaleidoscopic collection of delicious fodder. Plump for a pastrami bagel or sourdough grilled cheese, or hit full-on feast mode and indulge in a wedge of cake and sugar-high thickshake. Visit on the last Friday of the month for cocktails, craft beer and Sussex sparkling wine.

ESTABLISHED
2016

KEY ROASTER
Lindfield Coffee Works

BREWING METHOD
Espresso, pourover, batch filter

MACHINE
La Marzocco Linea PB

GRINDER
Mythos One, Mahlkonig EK43

OPENING HOURS
Mon-Sat 8.30am-5pm

www.lindfieldcoffeeworks.co.uk T: 01444 482140
f @lindfieldcoffee @lindfieldcoffeeworks

№38 STOOGE COFFEE

4 Trinity Street, Hastings, East Sussex, TN34 1HG

Nestling among the arty businesses, eclectic shops and cultural thrum of America Ground, Stooge Coffee is a laid-back find with a suitably indie attitude.

The interior is pared-back but inviting and plays host to a free-spirited, creative crowd drawn in by the enticing aroma of daily changing beans prepped as V60, woodneck and espresso.

TIP ENJOY THE SUBTLE SPICING OF A STOOGE TURMERIC LATTE OR PRANA MASALA CHAI

The friendly Stooge baristas are passionate about their work and always up for a spot of coffee chat. They'll guide you to your perfect cup and, if you're looking to up your home-brewing game, happily advise on the equipment and coffee on sale in-store.

Beans for both the Aurelia machine and the brew bar travel a short distance along the seafront from Hove's Pharmacie Coffee and will be joined this year by additional guest roasts.

To meet growing demand for the famed sourdough focaccia, a kitchen is being developed and there's also a snug in the pipeline so customers can commune with their coffee (and their thoughts) in comfort.

ESTABLISHED
2017

KEY ROASTER
Pharmacie
Coffee Roasters

BREWING METHOD
Espresso, V60,
woodneck,
cold brew

MACHINE
Nuova Simonelli
Aurelia II

GRINDER
Mahlkonig
K30 Air,
Mahlkonig EK43

OPENING HOURS
Mon-Fri 9am-4pm
Sat 10am-5pm

---

www.stoogecoffee.com   T: 01424 426710

f @stoogecoffee   @ @stoogecoffee

№39 URBAN GROUND

56 South Street, Eastbourne, East Sussex, BN21 4XB

With nine years under their belts and thousands of flat whites sunk at their Eastbourne cafe, the Urban Ground gang have certainly perfected the craft of serving quality caffeine.

Pioneers they may be but jaded they're not, and the team – which includes members of the original crew – still take great pains to ensure that every coffee, cake and sandwich that crosses the counter hits the mark.

TIP GET A SECOND SERVING OF URBAN GROUND AT NEARBY BOLTON ROAD

The Square Mile house espresso rotates seasonally to reflect the global harvest and each shot is meticulously weighed. There's also a single origin batch brew which showcases indie roasters from across the country. If you take your coffee with milk you'll be served the real deal from nearby Northiam Dairy, while free-from folk can choose from oat, almond or soy.

A cracking food offering includes house staples like pastrami flatbread with mustard mayo, pickles and spinach, freshly made soups and homemade bakes (turning down a slice of the banana loaf is not advised).

ESTABLISHED
2011

KEY ROASTER
Square Mile
Coffee Roasters

BREWING METHOD
Espresso,
batch filter,
cold brew

MACHINE
La Marzocco
Linea,
La Marzocco
Linea PB Auto
Brew Ratio

GRINDER
Mythos One,
Mahlkonig
Tanzania

OPENING HOURS
Mon-Sat **8**am-**5**pm
Sun **9**am-**5**pm

Gluten FREE

BEANS AVAILABLE INSTORE

WIFI

OUTDOOR seating

DISABLED ACCESS

COFFEE COURSES

www.urbanground.co.uk   T: 01323 398221

f @urbangroundeb   🐦 @urbangroundeb   📷 @urbangroundeb

MAP№ 40 PELICANO COFFEE CO. – THE LEVEL

The Level, St Peters Place, Brighton, East Sussex, BN1 4SA

For Venice Beach vibes in the heart of Brighton, head to the terrace of Pelicano's outpost at The Level and soak up the sun and sweet, sweet coffee.

When the weather's good and the doors are flung open, the heady scent of gently bronzing beans teams up with the waft of freshly ground coffee to lure passersby inside the compact set up.

TIP STOCK UP ON BEANS FOR YOUR HOME SUPPLY FROM THE RETAIL SECTION

The seasonal selection of blends and micro-lot coffees for the three Pelicano sites (find the other two on Sydney Street and Queens Road) are roasted here on a restored vintage Probat.

Sample the latest beans via a caboodle of filter kit or sink a 'spro which has been slung from the slick Synesso Cyncra machine.

If you're planning to kick back and spend time with friends over coffee, do it in full Pelicano style and pair your order with one of the carby treats on the countertop.

ESTABLISHED
2014

KEY ROASTER
Pelicano
Coffee Co.

BREWING METHOD
Espresso, V60,
AeroPress,
Chemex,
cold brew

MACHINE
Synesso Cyncra

GRINDER
Mythos One,
Mahlkonig EK43

OPENING HOURS
Mon-Sun **8**am-**6**pm
(reduced in winter)

---

www.pelicanocoffee.com   T: 07873 522613

f @pelicanohouse   🐦 @pelicanocoffee   📷 @pelicano.coffee.co

MAP 41 PELICANO COFFEE CO. – SYDNEY STREET

28 Sydney Street, Brighton, East Sussex, BN1 4EP

Getting lost in The Lanes is part of the fun for Brighton first timers, but if you're the kind of coffee head who likes to be armed with the deets on where to find the closest speciality fix, pin this spot on your Google Maps.

Turn your gaze from the maze of attention-grabbing shopfronts and look for the signature illustration above the door to find good coffee and chilled vibes.

TIP HEAD TO THE SECRET GARDEN TO SIP GOOD COFFEE ALFRESCO

Its flagship outlet (there's a smattering across the city) is where the story began in 2014 after founders Zephir Thomas and Sol Lee returned from Australia to set up their own speciality space. Fast-forward six years and the small coffee shop has sprouted two sister venues, taken the roasting operation in-house and started supplying other businesses with Brighton-roasted beans.

Coffee is the main attraction here, so don't visit in search of the full brunch experience. Instead, pair your order from the brew bar with a slab of one of the killer cakes.

ESTABLISHED
2014

KEY ROASTER
Pelicano
Coffee Co.

BREWING METHOD
Espresso,
AeroPress,
Kalita Wave,
Chemex, V60

MACHINE
La Marzocco
Strada

GRINDER
Mythos One,
Mahlkonig EK43

OPENING HOURS
Mon-Fri 8am-7pm
Sat-Sun 9am-7pm

www.pelicanocoffee.com   T: 07873 522613

f @pelicanohouse   🐦 @pelicanocoffee   ⬚ @pelicano.coffee.co

MAP № 42 640EAST – BRIGHTON

39 Upper Gardner Street, Brighton, East Sussex, BN1 4AN

Photo: Karoliina Helosuo and 640East

Having established a dedicated fanbase at its London and Bristol outlets, 640East decided to strike out for the coast, setting up shop in the heart of Brighton.

Like its sister cafes, 640East – Brighton is distinguished by its contemporary interior design with industrial edge. Look out for the red-neon signage which has become something of a trademark.

TIP THE TART REFRESHMENT OF HOME-BREWED KOMBUCHA AND KEFIR OFFERS AN ALTERNATIVE TO COFFEE

Thanks to the team's collaboration with London roastery Caravan, regulars can rely on a hit of the highest quality. Beans are sustainably sourced, fairly traded and environmentally light-footed – and brewed with distinction by a bevy of expert baristas.

In addition to espresso, a rotating roster of single origins gets the pourover treatment via V60, Kalita and AeroPress preps.

A seasonal curation of small plates and specials makes sticking around for something to eat a tempting option. Watch the chefs rustle up plant-based buddha bowls and epic crispy pork belly in the open-plan kitchen.

ESTABLISHED
2019

KEY ROASTER
Caravan Coffee Roasters

BREWING METHOD
Espresso, V60, AeroPress, Kalita Wave

MACHINE
La Marzocco Linea

GRINDER
Mythos

OPENING HOURS
Mon-Wed 8am-9.30pm
Thu-Sat 8am-11pm
Sun 11am-8pm

 BEANS AVAILABLE INSTORE

 WIFI

 DISABLED ACCESS

 BRING YOUR OWN cup

www.640east.co.uk   T: 07802 835994
f @640east   @ @640east

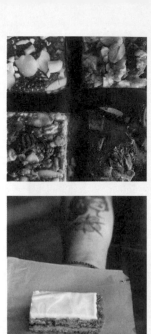

CAKESMITHS

CAKES FOR COFFEE SHOPS

www.cakesmiths.com

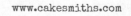

cakesmithsHQ | #Cakesmiths.HQ | @CakesmithsH

MAP 43 PELICANO COFFEE CO. – QUEENS ROAD

28 Queens Road, Brighton, East Sussex, BN1 3XA

Located mere minutes from Brighton train station, this Queens Road venue is the obvious first stop on any caffeinated tour of the seaside city.

Arrive early to join the throng of business-types and students forming an orderly queue at the custom Synesso machine for their first flat white of the day. Alternatively, make a more leisurely visit after rush hour to enjoy a V60 and freshly baked croissant on the bench out front or reclining on the leather couch.

TIP PICK UP A CUSTOM TEE AND REP PELICANO ON YOUR COFFEE TRAVELS

Whether you go 'spro or filter, there's a good line-up of beans to choose from with everything roasted on the 12kg cast iron Probat at Pelicano's outpost at The Level. The busy little roastery not only supplies the family of three espresso bars in Brighton but also takes care of a host of customers across the South East.

Pick up a bag (stamped with Pelicano's custom illustrations) from the retail selection to brew at home. Or, if you really want to up your game, join one of the coffee courses held in the basement lab.

ESTABLISHED
2018

KEY ROASTER
Pelicano
Coffee Co.

BREWING METHOD
Espresso, V60,
AeroPress,
Chemex,
cold brew

MACHINE
Synesso Cyncra

GRINDER
Mythos One,
Mahlkonig EK43

OPENING HOURS
Mon-Sun **8**am-**6**pm

Gluten FREE

BEANS AVAILABLE INSTORE

WIFI

OUTDOOR Seating

BRING YOUR OWN Cup

COFFEE COURSES

DOG FRIENDLY

---

www.pelicanocoffee.com   T: 07873 522613

f @pelicanohouse   🐦 @pelicanocoffee   📷 @pelicano.coffee.co

MAP №44 BOND ST. COFFEE

15 Bond Street, Brighton, East Sussex, BN1 1RD

Conscious coffee drinkers will be pleased to know that for every kilogram of Rwandan and Kenyan coffee served at this Brighton coffee shop, a tree is planted as part of reforestation project One Tree Planted.

Doing your bit for the planet is only one reason to seek out this quirkily furnished cafe. Speciality followers also gather here for the ever-changing menu of single origins which highlight unusual flavour profiles.

INSIDER TIP INVEST IN A REUSABLE CUP AND GET YOUR FIRST FLAT WHITE OR LATTE FREE

The caffeine hit comes with a sparkling conscience, too: beans are ethically sourced from privately owned farms and co-operatives before being roasted at Bond St.'s own roastery, Horsham. There are usually at least two single origins on espresso, with further bean dilemmas for those opting for a delicately aromatic filter.

The brunch menu inveigles visitors to stick around for the likes of celeriac and ham hock hash oozing with Plaw Hatch extra mature cheddar, or a fluffy pancake stack dripping with salted caramel sauce. Nearly everything is baked or prepared from scratch in-house and there are plenty of temptations for plant-based diners.

ESTABLISHED
2014

KEY ROASTER
Horsham Coffee Roaster

BREWING METHOD
Espresso, batch brew, AeroPress

MACHINE
La Marzocco Strada

GRINDER
Mahlkonig EK43, Ceado E37T x 2

OPENING HOURS
Mon-Fri 8am-5.30pm
Sat 9am-6pm
Sun 10am-4.30pm

Gluten FREE

BEANS AVAILABLE INSTORE

OUTDOOR seating

BRING YOUR OWN cup

DOG FRIENDLY

---

www.bondstcoffee.co.uk
f @bondstcoffee   @ @bondstcoffee

№45 TWIN PINES COFFEE

11 St James's Street, Brighton, East Sussex, BN2 1RE

Look out for the black shopfront on busy St James's Street to discover an ornate speciality experience.

The Twin Pines team aim to serve an unrivalled cup so work closely with their roaster of choice, Cast Iron, to constantly improve and deliver something rather unusual for their band of loyal locals. The result of this combined effort is house blend Enfoque Kaizen: a Brazilian-Colombian-Ethiopian hybrid which delivers a hit of sweetness, whether served with or without milk.

INSIDER TIP
REFRESH WITH NATURAL SODA, KOMBUCHA AND FREE SPARKLING WATER

An ever-changing selection of single origin guests from UK and European roasters also keeps the regulars up to date on roasting trends. Wherever the beans hail from, the team favour a medium-light roast style and serve them via hand-brew methods such as V60.

If opting for espresso, you'll find it pulled through a Slayer (called Buffy, of course) which is fully manual and relies on the baristas' art of stepping on or off the brew pressure according to the beans' needs.

An array of all-vegan cakes and savouries, plus an on-point playlist, further amplifies the experience.

ESTABLISHED
2016

KEY ROASTER
Cast Iron
Coffee Roasters

BREWING METHOD
Espresso, V60

MACHINE
Slayer V3 3G

GRINDER
Mahlkonig Peak,
Mahlkonig EK43

OPENING HOURS
Mon-Fri 8am-6.30pm
Sat 9am-7pm
Sun 10am-6pm

 Gluten FREE

 BEANS AVAILABLE / INSTORE

 OUTDOOR Seating

 DISABLED ACCESS

 BRING YOUR OWN Cup

 DOG FRIENDLY

---

www.twinpinescoffee.com

f @twinpinescoffee @ @twinpinescoffee

ROASTERIES

MAP 46 HORSHAM COFFEE ROASTER

The Studio, Howards Nursery, Handcross Road, Plummers Plain, West Sussex, RH13 6NX

Most speciality businesses have humble beginnings, and this roastery started out on a 1kg roaster in founders Bradley and Amelia Steenkamp's garage.

After a lot of tinkering to get the roast just right, the duo took their beans to Horsham Market where they acquired such a following of speciality fans that within a year they had outgrown their stall and decided to turn their focus to increasing both capacity and quality.

'THE FIRST ROASTERY TO SIGN THE TRANSPARENCY COFFEE PLEDGE'

Today, Horsham is a major player on the South East coffee scene and licensed Q grader Bradley is unusual in that he sources most of the beans direct from producers. Horsham is also the first roastery in the UK to sign the Transparency Coffee Pledge.

Directly traded beans from Costa Rica, Rwanda, Kenya and Brazil are carefully bronzed on a low-emission (60 per cent less than standard) Loring S35 and customers can visit the roastery to sample the latest lots.

ESTABLISHED
2012

ROASTER
MAKE & SIZE
Loring S35

CAFE ONSITE

OPEN TO THE PUBLIC

BEANS AVAILABLE
ONLINE   ONSITE

www.horshamcoffeeroaster.co.uk   T: 01403 892558
f @horshamcoffeeroaster   @horshamcoffee   @horshamcoffee

MAP 47 LINDFIELD COFFEE WORKS

70 High Street (via Alma Road), Lindfield, West Sussex, RH16 2HL

Every aspect of this Sussex set-up aims to benefit people throughout the coffee chain, from the farmers to the coffee-sippers – many of whom enjoy exploring the fruits of Lindfield's labours at the roastery's in-house coffee bar.

This year owner Kris Whelan made another trip to origin to forge closer links with Colombian producers, source greens and provide tools to help farmers. Just under half of the roaster's coffees are directly sourced from three farms in Antioquia, Colombia, while additional beans from Africa, South America and Asia arrive via import partners.

'BUYING BEANS HELPS NARROW THE GULF OF INEQUALITY'

Buying a bag of Lindfield beans helps narrow the gulf of inequality in coffee-growing regions, build a stable price for greens and, in turn, improve growers' quality of life.

The roastery and cafe will undergo a refurb this year while packaging will receive a brand refresh and become fully recyclable.

ESTABLISHED
2015

ROASTER
MAKE & SIZE
Giesen 6kg

CAFE
ONSITE

BEANS
AVAILABLE
ONLINE ONSITE

www.lindfieldcoffeeworks.co.uk   T: 01444 482140
f @lindfieldcoffee   **◎** @lindfieldcoffeeworks

MAP: 48 PELICANO COFFEE CO.

The Level, St Peters Place, Brighton, East Sussex, BN1 4SA

Speciality roasteries usually reside in the industrial outskirts of big cities, so to find one smack bang in the centre of Brighton is pretty niche.

Just a short stroll from the shore, Pelicano's roastery cafe at The Level is a busy hive of activity; regulars scuttle through picking up flat whites to-go; tourists throng on the outside seating when the sun's out; and locals stop by after work to buy beans to brew at home.

'HEAR THE GENTLE CHUG OF BEANS IN THE DRUM'

With a newly refurbished 1980s Probat bronzing beans right there in the cafe it's a great place to witness the process first hand. The behind-bar roaster serves the three Pelicano outposts across the city as well as a lengthy list of wholesale customers. On most days visitors will hear the gentle chug of beans in the drum alongside the hip-hop playlist.

The house blend Smokey Bird has become a stalwart on the menu. It changes seasonally, depending on the coffee harvest, while rotating single origins keep the filter options fresh and interesting.

ESTABLISHED
2014

ROASTER
MAKE & SIZE
Probat LP12

www.pelicanocoffee.com   T: 07873 522613

f @pelicanohouse   @pelicano.coffee.co

MAP№ 49 PHARMACIE COFFEE ROASTERS

18b Cambridge Grove, Hove, East Sussex, BN3 3ED

There are two certainties at Pharmacie: the first is that the coffee is always first rate and the second is that the ethics are 100 per cent sound – twin pillars that work symbiotically to deliver brews that both taste good and do good.

All of the fully traceable, speciality-grade arabica beans (chosen to surprise and delight) are seasonally sourced for peak freshness. The team then take the roasting approach of gently coaxing out the greens' inherent flavours rather than overdoing the roast.

Omni-roasting is not a thing at Pharmacie and, at each stage of the process, the crew keep in mind the brew method for which each batch of beans is destined. Espresso emerges well balanced; filters ring with fruity clarity.

'OMNI-ROASTING IS NOT A THING AT PHARMACIE'

Ever community-minded, the team hire out their Giesen W15 for slot-roasting in the belief that this kind of skill-sharing helps spread the passion for speciality.

ESTABLISHED
2015

ROASTER
MAKE & SIZE
Giesen W15

OPEN
BY APPOINTMENT

BEANS
AVAILABLE
ONLINE ONSITE

---

www.pharmacie.coffee   T: 01273 207674

f @pharmaciecoffee   🐦 @pharmaciecoffee   📷 @pharmacie_coffee_roasters

MAP 50 CAST IRON COFFEE ROASTERS

Unit 1-3, Quell Farm, Greatham Lane, Greatham, Pulborough, West Sussex, RH20 2ES

Selecting the best of the seasonal coffee crop is an essential step in Cast Iron's tried-and-tested roasting method.

Based in the heart of South Downs National Park, the family team only buy coffee from traceable sources and work exclusively with farmers who strive for excellence in every harvest. These high standards ensure that every Cast Iron coffee has been picked, washed and transported with care.

'THE ROASTERY RECENTLY EXPANDED THE WORKSHOP SPACE AND INSTALLED A NEW TRAINING AREA'

Equal attention is paid to the roasting process which takes place on a duo of Giesens. To meet increasing demand, the roastery recently expanded the workshop space and installed a new training area where coffee-curious visitors can learn the tricks of the trade. The clan also found time to compete in the recent SCA UK Brewers Cup and Barista Championship – reaching the finals in both.

ESTABLISHED
2015

ROASTER
MAKE & SIZE
Giesen W6
Giesen W15

OPEN BY APPOINTMENT

COURSES

CUPPING EVENTS

BEANS AVAILABLE
ONLINE ONSITE

---

www.castironroasters.com T: 07974 922860

f @castironcoffeeroasters 🐦 @castironroaster 📷 @castironroaster

USE SOUTHSEA ESPRESSO WEEKLY
THIOPIAN BUTUCHA
UATEMALA WAYKAN

SPRESSO THAT WE THINK YOU WILL LOVE
LE ORIGIN EL SALVDORIAN
TED BY THE BARN

D DRINKS DECAF
LE ORIGIN COLOMBIAN CALDONO
TED BY CAMPBELL & SYME

RE HERD AT NORTHNEY FARM

ALMOND MILK OR OAT MILK

WEEKLY
FFEES FROM UK & EUROPEAN ROASTERS
ER USING AEROPRESS & V6O

KID
BABYCCINO   1.0
HOT CHOCOLATE   2.4
SQUASH   0.8
MILKSHAKE   2.5-2.9
MILK   1.0

RETAIL
AEROPRESS   28
V60 CERAMIC   25
    PLASTIC   9
GLASS DECANTER   12
                     95
                      6

HAMPSHIRE

Nº53
Southsea Coffee

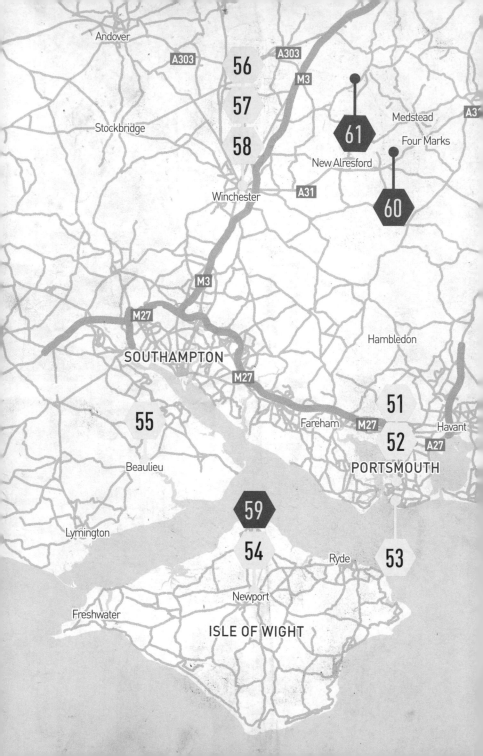

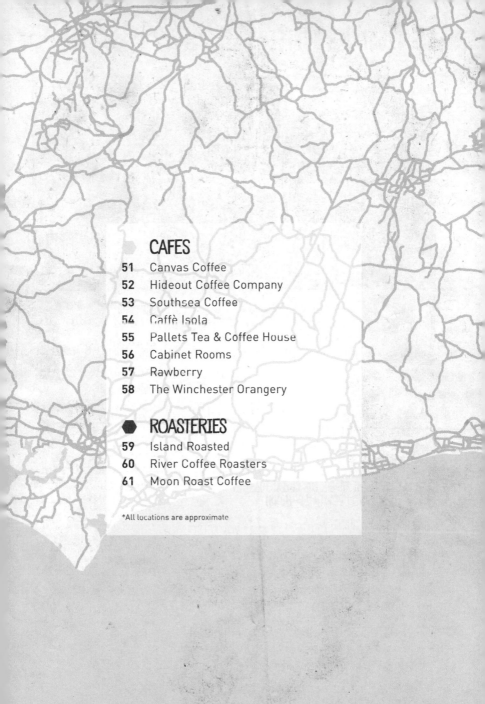

CAFES

ROASTERIES

*All locations are approximate

MAP№ 51 CANVAS COFFEE

Portsmouth & Southsea Railway Station, Portsmouth, Hampshire, PO1 1EQ

It's difficult enough to find decent coffee at railway stations, let alone award winning independent speciality coffee shops which roast their own beans. So, with Canvas Coffee brewing the good stuff in the middle of Portsmouth & Southsea station, the commuters passing through are on to a very good thing.

The social enterprise has run as a pop-up operation in the building for over six years, but 2020 will see the gang sign on the dotted line to make their stay more permanent, and renovation plans are afoot to make the space even more Insta-worthy.

☞TIP SAMPLE THE TO-DIE-FOR CHEESE TOASTIES (WHICH INCLUDE VEGAN OPTIONS)

Canvas' social mission is to help those in early recovery from drug and alcohol addiction by offering volunteer opportunities and barista training courses.

The crew began bean bronzing four years ago under the name Sunday Coffee Roasters, providing the filter coffee that's given the batch brew treatment in a customised Curtis (it's also available to buy on the retail shelf). It sits side-by-side with the Drake espresso blend from Winchester's The Roasting Party, which makes silky flat whites and other milk-based coffees.

ESTABLISHED
2014

KEY ROASTER
Multiple roasters

BREWING METHOD
Espresso, batch brew, cold brew

MACHINE
La Marzocco Linea PB

GRINDER
La Marzocco Vulcano, Mythos One, Mahlkonig EK43

OPENING HOURS
Mon-Fri 6am-6pm
Sat 7am-5pm

---

www.canvascoffee.co.uk   T: 07578 753364

f @canvascoffee   🐦 @mynewcanvas   📷 @mynewcanvas

MAP № 52 HIDEOUT COFFEE COMPANY

Unit 8, Charter House, Lord Montgomery Way, Portsmouth, Hampshire, PO1 2SB

Going against the grain since 2017, Hideout isn't exactly your identikit coffee house set-up.

The two-fingers-to-convention coffee and doughnut shop started out as Southsea's worst-kept secret, dishing out the finest dough and 'spros from the basement of the ilovedust design studio. As word spread, so did demand, and the gang moved to roomier digs in August 2019.

The resulting caffeine and sugar dispensary is a collision of design culture which, somehow, works. Upstairs, old-school tattoo typography goes back-to-back with a Scandi vibe that's all houseplants and dark wood. Below ground, Kubrick-inspired candy pink walls contrast with a statement tiled floor in the additional seating space.

INSIDER'S TIP — HIDEOUT'S INSTA FEED COMES WITH AN 18+ RATING – AND NOT JUST FOR THE 'SLUTTY DOUGHNUTS'

While the interiors are a draw for design dweebs, it's the River espresso and freshly fried dough that have acquired a cult following. Pick between the house espresso and guest from the Hampshire roastery, then pair it with one of the cake flavour combos which are as diverse as the mixtape playlist. Past sellouts include cherry bakewell, coconut cream 'n' lime, and fried chicken with tabasco.

ESTABLISHED
2017

KEY ROASTER
River Coffee Roasters

BREWING METHOD
Espresso

MACHINE
La Marzocco Linea Classic

GRINDER
Mahlkonig K30 Vario, DIP DK-30

OPENING HOURS
Mon-Fri 8am-6pm
Sat 9am-5pm

BEANS AVAILABLE INSTORE

WIFI

CYCLE FRIENDLY

DISABLED ACCESS

DOG FRIENDLY

---

www.hideoutcoffeeco.com   T: 02392 839916

f @hideoutcoffeecompany   🐦 @hideoutcoffeeco   📷 @hideoutcoffeecompany

MAP 53 SOUTHSEA COFFEE

63 Osborne Road, Portsmouth, Hampshire, PO5 3LS

Ask a local where to find great speciality coffee and scrumptious food in Southsea and it's odds on that they'll point you in the direction of this longstanding fave.

Tara and Martyn Knight established the popular hub in 2013 and their passion for good food, fun vibes and a cracking cup of coffee has elicited happy hums from loyal patrons and seaside day-trippers ever since.

TIP: CURBING YOUR CARNIVOROUS CRAVINGS? ADD A SIDE OF COCONUT BACON TO YOUR EGGS ORDER

London roastery Campbell & Syme supplies the house espresso, while a regularly updated line-up of guests provides lots of options on the brew bar. Tara and Martyn let cupping sessions guide their roastery choices and South West stalwarts Colonna, Crankhouse and Clifton have all featured on the board.

The same high standards are upheld when it comes to food. Everything on the menu is made from scratch, including the house Southsea buns – a take on chelsea buns – which ooze with homemade frangipane, blackberry jam, almonds and sour cherries. Savoury specials include tostada, tacos and pad thai salad.

ESTABLISHED
2013

KEY ROASTER
Campbell & Syme

BREWING METHOD
Espresso, V60, AeroPress

MACHINE
Conti Monte Carlo

GRINDER
Nuova Simonelli Mythos One, Mahlkonig EK43

OPENING HOURS
Mon-Fri 8am-5pm
Sat 8.30am-5pm
Sun 9am-4pm

www.southseacoffee.co.uk   T: 02393 079501

f @southseacoffee   🐦 @southseacoffee   📷 @southseacoffee

MAP№ 54 CAFFÈ ISOLA

85a St James Street, Newport, Isle of Wight, PO30 1LG

Visitors to the Isle of Wight shouldn't have any trouble tracking down this speciality coffee and panini bar as its sunshine-yellow exterior and giant coffee-plant mural are hard to miss.

The two-storey emporium is a hub for food and drink enthusiasts and, while the ground floor features a huge island style bar serving own-roasted coffee and Italian-inspired food, the mezzanine level rocks a roastery and tea-blending set-up which keeps the adjacent shop expertly stocked. It also hosts training sessions for home brewers.

TIP CHECK OUT THE PACKED CALENDAR OF EVENTS AND WORKSHOPS

Even if you just pop in to browse the hefty retail selection, the fragrant waft of freshly ground coffee is too much of a draw to ignore. Submit by plumping for a house espresso: a unique blend of two coffees from the same farm in El Salvador which have been processed in different ways (one honey, one washed).

Whether you're visiting for a long and lazy lunch punctuated with espresso and comforting bowls of homemade Sicilian pasta, or stopping by for one of the regular live music sessions, the vibe is fun and friendly.

ESTABLISHED
2006

KEY ROASTER
Island Roasted

BREWING METHOD
Espresso,
filter, V60

MACHINE
Astoria Storm

GRINDER
Fiorenzato
F83 E XGi,
Fiorenzato F64
FVO

OPENING HOURS
Mon-Sat 7.30am-6pm
Sun 9am-5pm

Gluten FREE

BEANS AVAILABLE INSTORE

WIFI

DISABLED ACCESS

BRING YOUR OWN CUP

COFFEE COURSES

DOG FRIENDLY

---

www.islandroasted.co.uk   T: 01983 524800
f @caffeisola 🐦 @caffe_isola 📷 @caffeisola

BE CONTEMPORARY.
STAY TRADITIONAL.

We understand that speed of service is vital. That's why we created our unique & multi award winning chai infusion. Perfectly blended by a barista for a barista.

CAFFEINE FREE

VEGAN FRIENDLY

ALLERGEN FREE

100% NATURAL

HENNY & JOE'S

#1

C H A I

MASALA CHAI INFUSION

(HINDI; MIXED SPICE TEA)

HANDMADE IN BATH

500ML

APPROX 20 SERVINGS

Say hello, *we can chat all day!*
hello@hennyandjoes.co.uk | @hennyandjoes | hennyandjoes.co.uk

№ 55 PALLETS TEA & COFFEE HOUSE

High Street, Beaulieu, Brokenhurst, Hampshire, SO42 7YA

Speciality coffee spots are like gold dust in rural Britain, so it's no surprise that Beaulieu's indie cafe attracts visitors from across the county who are happy to travel for its caffeinated thrills.

The intoxicating scent of freshly pulled espresso and hot-from-the-oven scones is an enchanting draw and even tourists exploring the nearby New Forest detour to sample the goods and make themselves at home on the handcrafted pallet furniture.

The 18th century shop has been in the Ide family for over 30 years and taken many forms since its original guise as a florist shop. Current owner Dominic took over from his relatives in 2017 and decided to add a slice of speciality coffee culture to the historic High Street.

TIP PECKISH? HEAD TO THE COUNTER TO CHOOSE FROM A SMORGASBORD OF DELIGHTS

Keen to do the family proud and keep standards high, Dominic recently welcomed head barista Jass Goodman to the team and started working with local roastery Moon Roast. Try the house coffee as espresso or pourover, or learn to create lip-smackingly good brews at home by taking one of Jass' coffee workshops.

ESTABLISHED
2017

KEY ROASTER
Moon Roast

BREWING METHOD
Espresso,
AeroPress, V60,
Clever Dripper

MACHINE
La Marzocco
Linea PB

GRINDER
Fiorenzato F64,
Sanremo SR70

OPENING HOURS
Mon-Sun 9am-5pm

T: 01590 612409
 @palletscoffeehouse @pallets_beaulieu

MAP№ 56 CABINET ROOMS

2 De Lunn Buildings, Jewry Street, Winchester, Hampshire, SO23 8SA

Gary Whiter and Marcus Roe, co-founders of Cabinet Rooms, take their roles as creative ambassadors for Winchester pretty seriously.

Assigned the task of championing food and drink in the region, the gents are behind events such as Winchester Cocktail Week and the Ginchester Christmas Market. And, much to the joy of local caffeine connoisseurs, shouting about speciality is another prominent part of the pair's remit.

It all started with their foodie blog which, in 2017, metamorphosed into a bricks-and-mortar arts cafe and bar.

The 1940s-esque haven is now a magnet for creative types whose daydreaming and masterminding is fuelled by Extract's Original Espresso – with assistance from a monthly merry-go-round of guests including Moon Roast, Origin and Redemption.

TIP KEEP AN EYE OPEN FOR UPCOMING WELLBEING WORKSHOPS AND CREATIVE EVENTS

The caffeinated fun continues long after sundown. Join the Secret Underground Film Society or monthly book club and, when the cuppas turn into cocktails, don't miss a chance to sample a dairy-free Flat White Russian or Cabinet Rooms Cafe Martini.

ESTABLISHED
2017

KEY ROASTER
Extract Coffee
Roasters

BREWING METHOD
Espresso,
Chemex

MACHINE
Sanremo
Zoe Compact

GRINDER
Sanremo
SR50

OPENING HOURS
Tue-Thu 8am-10pm
Fri 8am-11pm
Sat 9am-11pm
Sun 10am-5pm

www.cabinetrooms.com   T: 01962 866480

f @cabinetroomswinchester   🐦 @cabinetrooms   📷 @cabinetrooms

MAP №57 RAWBERRY

52-54 St George's Street, Winchester, Hampshire, SO23 8AH

From the moment customers step across Rawberry's threshold they soak up the feelgood vibes, thanks to the light flooding in through floor-to-ceiling windows and smiley staff who are keen to chat.

The family-run set-up started life as a market stall and continues its mission to keep Winchester locals nourished with tempting veggie, vegan and free-from goodies.

INSIDER'S TIP: NO REQUEST IS TOO OUTLANDISH, SO IF YOU'RE CRAVING A PARTICULAR SMOOTHIE BLEND JUST ASK

Signature smoothies include The Detox (beetroot, basil, apple and spinach) and decadent Heaven on Earth (hazelnut milk, tahini, banana and cacao). However, when only caffeine will do, single origins from River Coffee are on hand. The direct-relationship roastery specialises in sourcing sustainably grown beans.

For a more unusual hit, turn to a Rawberry superfood turmeric or charcoal latte, or a beetroot infused hot choc. Milks include hazelnut, soya, oat and almond.

Breakfasts such as acai bowls and sweet-potato muffins are perfect fuel for a productive day, while lunch centres around stuffed bagels, and roast veg with quinoa.

ESTABLISHED
2014

KEY ROASTER
River Coffee Roasters

BREWING METHOD
Espresso

MACHINE
Sanremo Verona RS

GRINDER
Mazzer Luigi

OPENING HOURS
Mon-Sat 9am-5pm
Sun 10am-4pm

Gluten FREE · BEANS AVAILABLE INSTORE · WIFI · CYCLE FRIENDLY · OUTDOOR SEATING · DISABLED ACCESS · BRING YOUR OWN CUP · DOG FRIENDLY

---

www.rawberry.net   T: 07714 696607
f @rawberryuk   🐦 @rawberryuk   📷 @rawberryjuice

MAP№58 THE WINCHESTER ORANGERY

11 The Square, Winchester, Hampshire, SO23 9ES

When it's not practical to partake in the Japanese art of shinrin-yoku (forest bathing), this Winchester coffee shop provides a delightful and alternative way of indulging in a little arboraceous therapy.

The greenery-draped ceiling and walls of the unique oasis centre around a giant tree, creating a sylvan spot in which to sip its exclusive coffee blend. Blossom is a medley of Colombian, Brazilian and Ethiopian beans bronzed nearby at River Coffee.

Drink it via any number of filter prep styles or go classic flat white and enjoy the elaborate and eccentric latte art motifs executed by the Orangery's baristas.

WINCHESTER TIP
GET THE DEETS ON THE NEXT LATTE ART THROWDOWN ONLINE

Pair your pick with a few choice finds from a menu plump with delicious dishes which riff on the classics: think cooked brekkies, sandwiches, toasties and waffles.

Come evening, bon viveurs should kick off with a Pineapple Mojito or River Espresso Martini before exploring a smorgasbord of seasonal specials.

ESTABLISHED
2019

KEY ROASTER
River Coffee
Roasters

BREWING METHOD
Espresso, V60,
Chemex,
batch brew

MACHINE
La Marzocco
KB90

GRINDER
Mazzer Major,
Mahlkonig
EK43 S

OPENING HOURS
Sun-Wed **8**am-**6**pm
Thu-Sat **8**am-**11**pm

Gluten FREE

BEANS AVAILABLE
INSTORE

WIFI

DOG FRIENDLY

---

www.thewinchesterorangery.com   T: 01962 863300

f @orangerywinchester   @ @thewinchesterorangery

ROASTERIES

MAP 59 ISLAND ROASTED

Blackhouse Quays, Little London, Newport, Isle of Wight, PO30 5YH

This family-run roastery is a key player in the fleet of incredible food and drink independents that populates the Isle of Wight.

Since starting Island Roasted in 2010, Dan Burgess and his team have been relentless in their quest to create delicious coffee and use the latest tech to record and consistently recreate the optimum roast profile for each lot that lands in the roastery. The honours are then carried out on a Diedrich and a vintage Vittoria roaster.

'DAN IS PLANNING A TRIP TO EL SALVADOR'

The collection of blends and single origins that ensues is globetrotting in its scope and regularly features beans from Burundi, Tanzania, Rwanda and Honduras. The house blend is a marriage of beans (the same coffee processed in two different ways) from a farm in El Salvador with which Dan has traded for five years. The estate's owner visited the Isle in 2018 and Dan is planning a reciprocal trip this year. Sample the beans as a flat white at sister cafe Caffè Isola.

ESTABLISHED
2010

ROASTER
MAKE & SIZE
Vintage Vittoria
VT15

Diedrich IR12

OPEN
BY APPOINTMENT

COFFEE
COURSES

COURSES

BEANS
AVAILABLE

ONLINE

www.islandroasted.co.uk T: 01983 857670

f @islandroasted 🐦 @island_roasted 📷 @islandroasted

MAP NO 60 RIVER COFFEE ROASTERS

The Old Dairy, Ranscombe Farm, Barnetts Wood Lane, Alresford, Hampshire, SO24 9SF

There's no better way of understanding how something works than rolling your sleeves up and getting stuck in, and that's exactly how Will Harrigan launched his Hampshire roastery in 2018.

Having worked in the coffee industry for five years, Will travelled to South America in 2017 to learn about life at origin. During the year he visited nine countries and had a go at nearly every bean-based job going – from picking coffee cherries to processing at the mill.

'IT'S AMAZING TO SHARE THE STORIES OF THESE FARMERS'

Today, almost all of the beans he roasts at River are sourced from farmers he's met – either on his working gap year or on trips to origin he's made since. *'It's amazing to be able to share the stories of these farmers with our wholesale partners,'* says Will.

The River collection – including Source and Flow blends – is largely sourced from South and Central America, although there's often an Ethiopian single origin (a visit there is imminent, too) thrown into the mix.

ESTABLISHED
2018

ROASTER
MAKE & SIZE
Mill City 10kg

OPEN
BY APPOINTMENT

COFFEE
COURSES

BEANS
AVAILABLE
ONLINE

---

www.rivercoffeeroasters.com   T: 07954 177282

f @rivercoffeeuk   @rivercoffeeuk   @rivercoffeeuk

MAP 61 MOON ROAST COFFEE

Chilton Manor Farm, Chilton Candover, Alresford, Hampshire, SO24 9TX

Given his family background, it's no surprise that fourth-generation coffeesmith Francis Bradshaw couldn't resist the call of the grind. He's even named two of his Probat roasters after his rellies: his coffee-pro dad Haydon and great-grandfather RGB.

Francis runs Moon Roast from converted stables on a working farm in Hampshire where he sources the best speciality-grade beans from small farms in big-hitting coffee-growing countries including Rwanda, Kenya and Guatemala.

ESTABLISHED
2012

ROASTER
MAKE & SIZE
Probat P25

Probat P12

Probat sample
roaster 100g

'FOURTH-GENERATION COFFEESMITH FRANCIS COULDN'T RESIST THE CALL OF THE GRIND'

By joining the dots from grower to customer, Francis aims to deliver a gratifying drinking experience backed up by the reassurance of ethical sourcing where a fair price is paid to farmers.

Each lot is carefully profiled and roasted in small batches to draw out every last drop of flavour, while roasting wholesale orders on demand ensures peak freshness.

www.moonroast.co.uk   T: 01256 389996

f @moonroast   🐦 @moonroast   📷 @moonroastcoffee

WILTSHIRE
&DORSET

№63
Espresso Kitchen

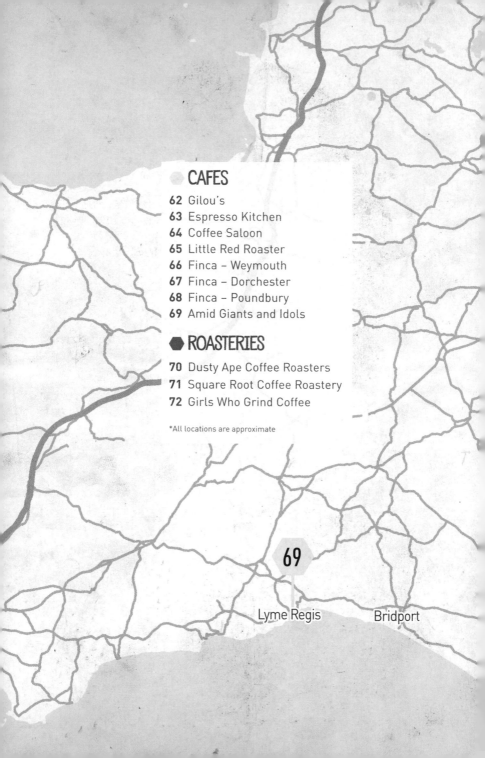

CAFES

ROASTERIES

*All locations are approximate

69

Lyme Regis   Bridport

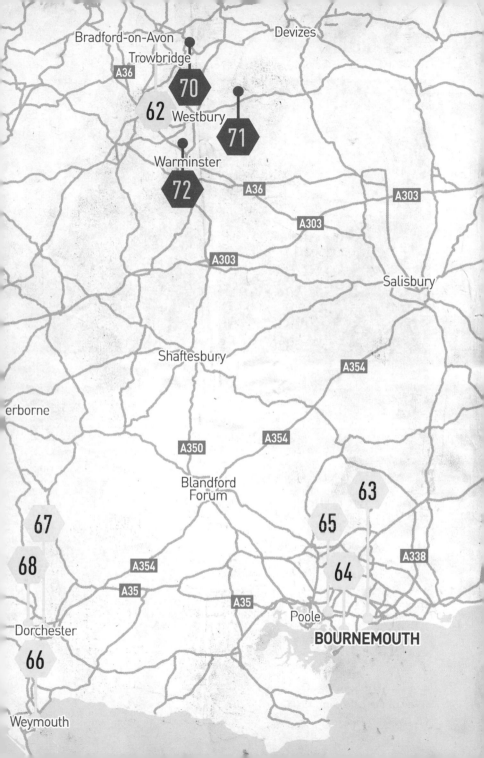

MAP №62 GILOU'S

4 The Shambles, Bradford-on-Avon, Wiltshire, BA15 1JS

Forget the ubiquitous antipodean vibe or American diner style, this Bradford-on-Avon coffee shop looks to French flair for its creative influences.

Gilou's daily offering of almond croissants, handmade gateaux and rustic ciabatta champion flavour. The enticing repertoire of bakes shifts with the season and has earnt the cafe a permanent spot in both local foodies and visiting coffee-lovers' good books.

INSIDER TIP IN SUMMER, FIGHT IT OUT FOR AN ALFRESCO SPOT ON THE SHAMBLES

While the recipes may be faithful to founder Gilles Defrance's forefathers, the coffee is fully third wave. Seasonal single origin espresso changes weekly and is sourced from the likes of Bailies in Belfast, Bath's Colonna, Round Hill in Somerset and Cornwall's Origin.

The best seats in the house are at the window bench where you can watch shoppers and tourists bustling past. Failing that, unwind with your pick of the counter bakes in one of the cosy Chesterfield armchairs.

ESTABLISHED
2016

KEY ROASTER
Origin Coffee Roasters

BREWING METHOD
Espresso, V60, AeroPress

MACHINE
La Marzocco FB80

GRINDER
Mythos One Clima Pro, Mazzer

OPENING HOURS
Mon-Tue, Thu-Sat
10am-**5**pm

Gluten FREE

BEANS AVAILABLE INSTORE

WIFI

CYCLE FRIENDLY

OUTDOOR SEATING

DISABLED ACCESS

BRING YOUR OWN CUP

www.gilouscafe.com T: 01225 862203

f @Gilou's @gilouscafe

ᴹᵃᵖ⁶³ ESPRESSO KITCHEN

69 Commercial Road, Bournemouth, Dorset, BH2 5RT

Every inch of this delightfully eccentric coffee shop houses an eye-catching piece of paraphernalia, from the walls pasted with newspapers, surfboards and postcards to the colanders, coffee tins and clash of cushions lining the wooden benches.

Having picked your poison from the espresso menu, choose a perch downstairs in the bustle of the bar or head up to the snug where you can scribble notes to other caffeine enthusiasts on the chalkboard wall.

TIP KEEP AN EYE OPEN FOR THE BURGEONING BILL OF COMMUNITY ACTIVITIES

Local roastery Beanpress stocks the hopper with a rich, sweet blend which is crafted into smooth espresso by skilled baristas. They're also on-point when it comes to latte art, working with dairy and three plant-based milks.

Pair your cup with a droolworthy treat of the edible kind: a cracking line-up of veggie, gluten-free, dairy-free and organic options (plus vegan toasties and cakes) feature on the menu. Or, if it's sweet gratification you're craving, hit up the counter of homemade bakes.

ESTABLISHED
2012

KEY ROASTER
Beanpress
Coffee Co.

BREWING METHOD
Espresso

MACHINE
La Marzocco
FB70

GRINDER
La Marzocco
Swift

OPENING HOURS
Mon-Sat **7.30**am-**7**pm
Sun **9**am-**6**pm

Gluten FREE

BEANS AVAILABLE
INSTORE

WIFI

OUTDOOR seating

BRING YOUR OWN Cup.

COFFEE COURSES

DOG FRIENDLY

---

www.espressokitchen.online   T: 01202 972420

f @espressokitchen   @ @espressokitchen

MAP №64 COFFEE SALOON

Canford Cliffs, Poole, Dorset, BH13 7LE

I n bringing a flavour of the wild west to the West Country, Coffee Saloon has played an important part in shaping the speciality scene across Dorset.

This Canford Cliffs favourite is one of four outposts (the others are in Wareham, Poole Old Town, Dorchester and Westbourne) where the espresso-slinging baristas wave the tamper for independence from big-chain mediocrity. Their weapon of choice is a gleaming La Marzocco machine, from which the experienced crew craft a sterling selection of espresso-based brews.

INSIDER'S TIP: FEELING THE HEAT? LET SMOOTHIES, MILKSHAKES AND ICED COFFEES COME TO THE RESCUE

As with the whole stable of Coffee Saloon venues, upcycled furniture and vintage design create a uniquely quirky space, while communal seating encourages chatter over a menu of toasties, cakes and bakes.

A venturesome array of vegan bites is freshly prepped each morning and includes the likes of croissants oozing with jam (made from apricots grown in Vesuvius National Park) and Saloon Cioccolata Slices fashioned using Italian Caffarel chocolate pastry.

ESTABLISHED
2014

KEY ROASTER
Origin Coffee Roasters

BREWING METHOD
Espresso

MACHINE
La Marzocco

GRINDER
Mythos One, Clima Pro

OPENING HOURS
Mon-Fri 7am-4pm
Sat-Sun 8am-4pm

Gluten FREE

BEANS AVAILABLE INSTORE

WIFI

CYCLE FRIENDLY

OUTDOOR seating

BRING YOUR OWN Cup

COFFEE COURSES

DOG FRIENDLY

---

www.coffeesaloon.com   T: 07384 110486

f @coffeesaloon   @thecoffeesaloons

ℳ65 LITTLE RED ROASTER
18 Station Road, Parkstone, Poole, Dorset, BH14 8UB

It's been a whopping ten years since the Little Red Roaster team opened the doors of their parkside hangout and invited in Poole's caffeine-conscious for top-notch coffee and handmade bagels.

During this decade of deliciousness their doughy delights have reached superstar status, attracting sourdough-seekers from far and wide. The own-roasted coffee is equally as popular, with freshly bronzed beans pulled through the Conti Monte Carlo machine as espresso. Or join the queue for the ultimate morning combo of batch brew and a breakfast bagel.

🄳🄸🄿 TAKE YOUR POOCH ALONG – FURRY FRIENDS ARE WELCOMED WITH OPEN PAWS

There's more than just the brews and bakes to tempt passersby into Little Red Roaster, however, as it also hosts regular creative events, film nights, a ukulele club, craft workshops and even a series of talks on opera.

To celebrate the tenth anniversary, the team have installed a working little red roaster in the cafe, and are returning to roasting small batches in-store as in the early years. A new 2kg Coffee-Tech will roast single origins so that the whirr and waft can be experienced by patrons as they sip a brew or wait for their order to-go.

ESTABLISHED
2010

KEY ROASTER
Beanpress Coffee Co.

BREWING METHOD
Espresso, Bunn Trifecta, Fetco batch brew

MACHINE
Conti Monte Carlo

GRINDER
Compak E8

OPENING HOURS
Mon-Fri 7am-5pm
Sat 8am-5pm
Sun 9am-2pm

www.littleredroaster.co.uk   T: 01202 240450
f @littleredcoffee   @littleredroaster

MAP 66 FINCA - WEYMOUTH

13 St Thomas Street, Weymouth, Dorset, DT4 8EW

In establishing its fourth (and latest) outpost, Finca has brought the welcome gift of fine coffee to downtown Weymouth.

The relaxed vibe and rustic-chic decor of the new cafe reflects the style of its sister coffee shops, thanks to the inclusion of natural wood and warm-glow lighting. The front windows can be flung wide open, letting customers – and the seductive aroma of ground beans – spill out onto the streetside seating.

INSIDER TIP ASK THE FRIENDLY STAFF FOR AN AT-HOME RECOMMENDATION FROM THE RETAIL SELECTION

Whether you opt for espresso, V60 or cold brew, you're assured of own-roasted beans which have been expertly selected and bronzed for flavour. Finca is a byword for seasonality so there are always two rotating single origins available. Savour your sip in the quiet of the snug or soak up some Dorset rays in the enclosed yard.

The Finca bakery at Poundbury supplies the range of enticing cakes (if you're dashing in for a takeaway, make sure you add a slice of the day's traybake to your order), along with crusty sourdough bread that's made into toasted sarnies.

ESTABLISHED
2019

KEY ROASTER
Finca Coffee
Roasters

BREWING METHOD
Espresso, V60,
cold brew

MACHINE
La Marzocco
Linea

GRINDER
Olympus

OPENING HOURS
Mon-Sat **8**am-**4**pm
Sun **10**am-**2**pm

Gluten FREE

BEANS AVAILABLE INSTORE

WIFI

OUTDOOR SEATING

DISABLED ACCESS

BRING YOUR OWN cup

---

www.fincacoffee.co.uk   T: 01305 300400

f @fincaweymouth   🐦 @scouting4coffee   📷 @scouting4coffee

MAP № 67 FINCA – DORCHESTER

41 Great Western Road, Dorchester, Dorset, DT1 1UF

On a leafy street near Dorchester town centre, you'll find a speciality coffee joint with an easygoing attitude. Big bi-fold windows display the fun and buzzy vibe within, revealing to any passerby that Finca is all about the good times.

The freshness of the coffee can never be faulted here as the beans travel a mere five minutes from Finca's nearby roastery. Small batches are processed by hand to tickle fruity and funky flavours from carefully selected small lots.

INSIDER'S TIP — TRY ONE OF THE TOASTIES – THEY MAKE EXCELLENT USE OF THE TEAM'S DELICIOUS HOMEMADE SOURDOUGH

There are always at least two single origins to try at the Dorchester cafe and the knowledgeable baristas use espresso, V60 and AeroPress methods to ensure every cup hits the exacting Finca standards.

Chase your hit with a crisp pastry (try the glossy cinnamon buns) or gooey cake (the brownies are legendary) crafted at the cafe's sister bakery in nearby Poundbury.

ESTABLISHED
2014

KEY ROASTER
Finca Coffee Roasters

BREWING METHOD
Espresso, V60, AeroPress

MACHINE
La Marzocco Linea

GRINDER
Olympus

OPENING HOURS
Mon-Sat 9am-4pm
Sun 10am-2pm

Gluten FREE

BEANS AVAILABLE INSTORE

WIFI

BRING YOUR OWN Cup

DOG FRIENDLY

www.fincacoffee.co.uk   T: 01305 300400

f @fincadorchester   🐦 @scouting4coffee   📷 @scouting4coffee

^{MAP}№⁶⁸ 68 FINCA – POUNDBURY

The Buttermarket, 24 Buttercross, Poundbury, Dorset, DT1 3AZ

When it comes to impressive locations, Finca has bagged a good'un in Poundbury. From its position in the rotunda at the top of The Buttermarket, it looks down across immaculate townhouses towards green fields. And, if you're quick off the mark, you can ease into a deckchair with your morning cuppa and take it all in from the roomy terrace.

Meticulously selected beans make the brief trip from Finca's Dorchester roastery where they're expertly roasted by hand. Expect seasonally changing single origins – around 20 varieties are given a whirl each year. In addition to the usual espresso suspects, you'll also find V60, AeroPress, cold brew and on-tap nitro for a palate-tingling caffeine hit.

TIP PICK UP A LOAF OF FRESHLY BAKED ORGANIC STONEGROUND SOURDOUGH BREAD ON YOUR VISIT

You'll discern the comforting fragrance of baking mingling with the aromas from the La Marzocco machine; that'll be the on-site bakers rustling up an array of imaginative cakes plus sourdough and organic bread. Be warned: the hot buttered toast is nigh-on irresistible.

ESTABLISHED
2017

KEY ROASTER
Finca Coffee
Roasters

BREWING METHOD
Espresso, V60,
AeroPress,
nitro, cold brew

MACHINE
La Marzocco

GRINDER
Olympus

OPENING HOURS
Mon-Sat 8am-4pm
Sun 10am-2pm

 Gluten FREE

 BEANS AVAILABLE INSTORE

 CYCLE FRIENDLY

 OUTDOOR SEATING

 BRING YOUR OWN Cup.

 COFFEE COURSES

 DOG FRIENDLY

www.fincacoffee.co.uk   T: 01305 300400

f @fincapoundbury   🐦 @scouting4coffee   @ @scouting4coffee

MAP №69 AMID GIANTS AND IDOLS

59 Silver Street, Lyme Regis, Dorset, DT7 3HR

This Silver Street hub has been a beacon of speciality coffee on the Dorset coast for over half a decade, keeping tourists and locals at peak caffeination levels.

Steve and Elaine Naylor took over the popular coffee shop in 2016 and have continued its good work in showcasing exceptional coffees from regional roasters. Single origins and blends from Exeter's Crankhouse and Brazier in Somerset regularly rotate on the two Mazzer grinders. And, if you like what you're drinking, the team are also happy to grind beans to your preferred brew style so you can craft your own artisan coffee at home.

TIP THIS IS A SUPER DOG-FRIENDLY SPOT – TAKE YOUR POOCH AFTER A WALK ON THE BEACH

A wholesome menu of vegan soups and homemade cakes makes sticking around to flick through a magazine, or challenge a friend to a game of draughts, rather tempting. The indulgent hot choc dusted with chilli flakes, vanilla and cinnamon is another good reason to hang around after you've sunk your first coffee.

ESTABLISHED
2014

KEY ROASTER
Multiple roasters

BREWING METHOD
Espresso, V60, AeroPress, woodneck

MACHINE
La Marzocco

GRINDER
Mazzer x 2

OPENING HOURS
Mon-Sun **10**am-**4**pm
(closed Tuesdays in winter)

---

www.amidgiantsandidols.co.uk   T: 01297 443791

f @amidgiants   🐦 @amidgiantsidols

ROASTERIES

Nº72
Girls Who Grind Coffee

MAP 70 DUSTY APE COFFEE ROASTERS

Unit 1, Marsh Farm Industrial Estate, Hilperton, Wiltshire, BA14 7PJ

Rocco 'cook'

Phil 'sensei'

Mamiko 'perfectionist'

Abi 'trailblazer'

Sarah 'appropriate adult'

Wiltshire's original speciality coffee roaster has recently unveiled a spanking new on-site coffee bar. Now imbibers can pull up a stool and settle in for a brew made from beans that have travelled mere metres from the drum in which they were roasted.

Coffee fans have long swooned over Dusty Ape's kaleidoscopic collection of ethically sourced small-batch roasts so this development provides a unique glimpse into the gang's obsession with teasing out maximum flavour.

'A SPANKING NEW ON-SITE COFFEE BAR'

The roster of palate-expanding delights continues to grow as the crew experiment with more coffees. For a burst of chocolate check out the Santa Leticia which is grown in the Mayan coffee gardens of El Salvador. Naturals from Yirgacheffe and Uganda tick the "wild and wacky" box, while beans from farms including Colombia's La Esperanza deliver funky flavours.

And it's not just the range of beans that's flourishing: the team also recently welcomed two new recruits.

ESTABLISHED
2013

ROASTER
MAKE & SIZE
Probat 12kg
Toper 5kg
Probat 1kg

CAFE ONSITE

OPEN TO THE PUBLIC

COFFEE COURSES

BEANS AVAILABLE
ONLINE ONSITE

www.dustyape.com   T: 01225 753838
f @dustyapecoffee   🐦 @dustyape   📷 @dustyape

M.A.P. **71** SQUARE ROOT COFFEE ROASTERY

12 Station Yard, Edington, Wiltshire, BA13 4NT

Adrian Smith describes his Wiltshire roastery as a *'fortress of solitude'* where he can get lost in the immersive and sensory experience of crafting coffee, thanks to the whirr of the machine, the heady aroma and the astonishing new flavours to be discovered in every cupping session.

ESTABLISHED
2014

ROASTER
MAKE & SIZE
TX5

BEANS
AVAILABLE
ONLINE

'AN IMMERSIVE AND SENSORY EXPERIENCE'

Greens from Brazil, India, Indonesia, Tanzania and Peru (to name just a few regions) take turns in the custom-made 5kg Turkish roaster, which Adrian fills to a maximum of 3kg for optimum roast results. Exacting standards are also applied to sourcing and he works closely with importers to track beans from farm through to processing, storage and shipping, ensuring only the highest quality beans reach the Square Root roasting drum.

Taste the result of Adrian's labours at the roastery's cafe The Bath Coffee Company on the city's Kingsmead Square or order beans online to brew at home.

www.squarerootcoffee.co.uk T: 07940 120835
f @squarerootcoffee

MAP: 72 GIRLS WHO GRIND COFFEE

Unit 2, Millards Farm, Upton Scudamore, Warminster, Wiltshire, BA12 0AQ

By building a unique female-only supply chain, Girls Who Grind is blazing a girl-powered trail in the male-dominated world of coffee production.

Fi O'Brien and Casey LaLonde's aim is to achieve recognition for the work poured into the industry by women because, while their labour accounts for at least 70 per cent of the picking and sorting duties, women are rarely the decision makers.

Fi and Casey imagined a new reality, which they're making happen by exclusively seeking out beans from female producers and giving these farmers access to the speciality coffee market and opportunities to grow their businesses.

ESTABLISHED
2017

ROASTER
MAKE & SIZE
Giesen W6

OPEN
BY APPOINTMENT

BEANS
AVAILABLE

ONLINE

'AN UNUSUAL HIT OF BUBBLEGUM FRUITINESS'

For proof of the deliciousness of the resulting brews, check out GWGC's growing fanbase of indie coffee shops which serve its coffees. Butterscotch and pecan flavours come courtesy of single origin beans from El Salvador's Boza sisters, or try Xingang – produced in China by a mother and daughter team – for an unusual hit of bubblegum fruitiness.

www.girlswhogrindcoffee.com   T: 01985 211151

f @girlswhogrindcoffee   🐦 @gwg_coffee   📷 @girlswhogrindcoffee

BrIStOL

Nº75
Spicer+Cole

CAFES

ROASTERY

*All locations are approximate

MAP 73 TINCAN COFFEE CO – GLOUCESTER ROAD

157 Gloucester Road, Bishopston, Bristol, BS7 8BA

This little sister venue to the popular North Street site enjoys residence on Europe's longest stretch of indies – fitting for a cafe that only sources from other local businesses.

The sleek spot specialises in Bristol-roasted coffee (via Clifton) and serves a seasonal espresso and line-up of single origin guests. The baristas have perfected the art of pouring an excellent rosetta while simultaneously engaging in friendly chat and know all of their regulars' orders.

INSIDER'S TIP TINCAN'S TAKE-OUT CUPS ARE 100 PER CENT PLANT-BASED

While you won't find the full brunch experience here, your silky flat white can be kept company by all manner of incredible edibles – from homemade sausage rolls and savoury parcels (including vegan and veggie versions) to toasties and crumpets. Cakes and sweet pastries feature big-time, naturally.

In keeping with an emphasis on supporting the local community of foodie businesses, the team use ham from the butchers next door to craft scrummy toasties while the greengrocer on the other side provides all the plant-based produce – including fruit for the smoothies.

ESTABLISHED
2018

KEY ROASTER
Clifton Coffee Roasters

BREWING METHOD
Espresso, filter

MACHINE
La Marzocco Linea PB

GRINDER
Mythos One, Compak

OPENING HOURS
Mon-Sat **8**am-**6**pm
Sun **9**am-**5**pm

 Gluten FREE

 BEANS AVAILABLE INSTORE

 WIFI

 CYCLE FRIENDLY

 OUTDOOR Seating

 DISABLED ACCESS

BRING YOUR OWN Cup

 DOG FRIENDLY

---

www.tincancoffee.co.uk   **T:** 01179 232076

f @tincancoffeeco   🐦 @tincancoffeeco   📷 @tincancoffeeco

MAP 74 WEST STREET KITCHEN

55 West Street, St Philip's, Bristol, BS2 0BZ

Bristol's trendy Old Market is home to this charmingly authentic little gem which has been stripped back to expose its original bricks and patchwork of wooden floorboards.

Founders Millie (the cake baker) and Nathan (the coffee roaster) are purists when it comes to quality food and drink and, if they're not planning their next meal, they're planning yours via their weekly changing menus.

Produce from the Forest of Dean – the couples' original home region – features heavily, and that extends to the hoppers which showcase beans from James Gourmet Coffee. Nathan previously headed up the roasting operation at the Herefordshire roastery so coffee drinking visitors are in very safe hands.

INSIDERS TIP
MONTHLY SUPPER CLUBS PLAY WITH THE BEST LOCAL, SEASONAL PRODUCE

There's always a choice of single origins to explore via V60 (currently a naturally processed, lightly roasted Colombian), while Brazilian beans with their deep chocolatey flavour tend to star as the rich house espresso. For end-of-day sipping, make a beeline for the Kitchen's own full-bean-immersion coffee liqueur served as an exquisite Espresso Martini.

ESTABLISHED
2017

KEY ROASTER
James Gourmet Coffee

BREWING METHOD
Espresso, V60

MACHINE
La Marzocco Linea PB

GRINDER
Mahlkonig K30, Mahlkonig FK43

OPENING HOURS
Mon-Thu 11am-4pm
Fri 11am-10pm
Sat 10am-10pm

Gluten FREE

 BEANS AVAILABLE INSTORE

 WIFI

 OUTDOOR SEATING

 COFFEE COURSES

 DOG FRIENDLY

---

www.weststreetkitchen.co.uk   T: 07308 161621

f @weststreetkitchen   🐦 @weststreetkitch   📷 @west_street_kitchen

MAP № 75 SPICER+COLE

Old Temple Street/Counterslip, Finzels Reach, Bristol, BS1 6BX

Bristol's trio of Spicer+Cole cafes became a quartet last year when this latest outpost opened a stone's throw from the city's picturesque Castle Park.

It's not just dog walkers, cyclists and day-trippers who drop in to the cafe, however, as its location at the heart of a buzzy new waterfront development also sees it welcoming workers and residents who inhabit this slick urban quarter.

SPICER'S TIP SIZZLING OUTSIDE? PICK UP A COLD BREW AND HEAD TO THE PARK

The roomy space is a real-life incarnation of an "industrial chic" Pinterest board: trailing plants are highlighted against moody blue walls while contemporary metal light-fittings contrast with a time-worn parquet floor.

The caffeinated offering is equally sleek: fellow Bristol indie Extract provides the South American house blend, while guest single origins showcase a reel of talent from the likes of Ozone, The Barn, Climpson and Triple Co.

Pair your brew with a sweet something from the collection of jaw-dropping bakes or linger longer over a protein box (the hot smoked salmon with miso-marinated eggs is ace) or one of the daily-changing tarts, tortillas or salads.

ESTABLISHED
2019

KEY ROASTER
Extract Coffee Roasters

BREWING METHOD
Espresso, filter, cold brew

MACHINE
La Marzocco

GRINDER
Mythos One

OPENING HOURS
Mon-Fri
7.30am-**4.30**pm
Sat-Sun
8.30am-**4.30**pm

 Gluten FREE

 BEANS AVAILABLE INSTORE

 WIFI

 CYCLE FRIENDLY

 OUTDOOR seating

 DISABLED ACCESS

 BRING YOUR OWN Cup

---

www.spicerandcole.co.uk   **T:** 01179 304218

 f @spicerandcole 🐦 @spicerandcole 📷 @spicerandcole

MAP 76 SMALL STREET ESPRESSO

23 Small Street, Bristol, BS1 1DW

Don't be deterred if this central spot is packed out when you rock up, as it's nearly always overflowing with locals picking up a coffee to-go. Simply squeeze in with the regulars or join the all-weather patrons on the benches outside.

Such is the demand for take-out brews at Small Street that the team introduced the Hit and Run, an opportunity to sample the latest guest as espresso while you wait for your order. Round Hill, Yallah, Square Mile and Dark Arts have all featured on the list, going back-to-back with house roaster Clifton.

Stick around to watch the baristas juggle shots behind the custom sky-blue La Marzocco and treat yo'self to a slab of toasted banana bread with lashings of butter – the perfect pairing to a flat white crafted with local milk.

INSIDERS TIP PICK UP A HART'S BAKERY CROISSANT WITH YOUR PICCOLO TO-GO

In summer, cold brew is king. The Small Street gang take it pretty seriously, opting for the Coffega Tower as their brew method of choice. Take it straight up or pair the concentrated version with tonic for icy caffeinated refreshment.

ESTABLISHED
2012

KEY ROASTER
Clifton Coffee
Roasters

BREWING METHOD
Espresso, V60,
cold brew

MACHINE
La Marzocco
FB80

GRINDER
Mythos,
Mahlkonig EK43

OPENING HOURS
Mon-Fri 7.30am-4.30pm
Sat 9.30am-4.30pm

  Gluten FREE

 BEANS AVAILABLE / INSTORE

 WIFI

 OUTDOOR seating

 DISABLED & ACCESS

 BRING YOUR OWN cup

 DOG FRIENDLY

www.smallstreetespresso.co.uk

f @smallstespresso   🐦 @smallstespresso   📷 @smallstespresso

ETHICALLY SOURCED **EXTRACT** PERFECTLY CRAFTED

COFFEE ROASTERS

➤ PROUD TO SUPPORT

EMPIRE FIGHTING CHANCE

RAISING ASPIRATION &
HELPING YOUNG PEOPLE

SUPPORT IN
- BRISTOL
- GLOUCESTERSHIRE
- THE COTSWOLDS
- SOUTH WALES
- DEVON
- CORNWALL

EXTRACTCOFFEE.CO.UK

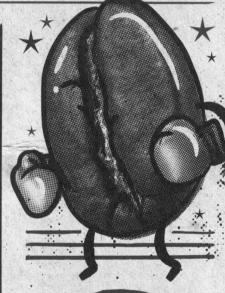

GROUNDSUP
E
CHARITY COLLECTIVE

MAP No. 77 SOCIETY CAFE – HARBOURSIDE

Farrs Lane, Narrow Quay, Bristol, BS1 4BD

When Adrian and Jane Campbell-Howard decided to expand their micro-empire beyond its home city of Bath, opening a speciality outpost in neighbouring indie-friendly Bristol was an obvious next move.

Happily, they found a fabulous harbourside venue ideally located within walking distance of both the creative city centre and the foodie havens of Wapping Wharf and Southville. It's spacious, too, with plenty of tables (inside and out) where speciality fans can catch up with friends, knuckle down to some work or browse the cultural literature which litters the cafe.

TIP DROP IN ON ONE OF THE REGULAR CUPPING SESSIONS

A long-term relationship with Cornwall's Origin Coffee keeps the grinders replete with seasonal beans, a few of the Society team even joined the roasters on a recent trip to meet farmers at origin in Nicaragua.

The espresso, batch brew and AeroPress opportunities are bolstered with guest coffees from the likes of Crankhouse, Bailies and Round Hill. In summer, pick up a cold brew to-go and join the crowds chilling out by the water.

ESTABLISHED
2017

KEY ROASTER
Origin Coffee
Roasters

BREWING METHOD
Espresso,
AeroPress,
cold brew,
batch brew

MACHINE
La Marzocco
Linea PB

GRINDER
Mahlkonig EK43,
Mythos One

OPENING HOURS
Mon-Sat 7.30am-6.30pm
Sun 9am-6pm

---

www.society-cafe.com **T:** 01179 304660

f @societycafebath **У** @societycafe **◎** @societycafe

MAP 78 640EAST – BRISTOL

Millennium Square Kiosk, Bristol, BS1 5DB

Photo: Karoliina Helosuo and 640East

Enjoying a prime position on Bristol's Millennium Square, the 640East kiosk comes with all the trappings of the London original. An upcycled-industrial aesthetic (highlights include a counter made from old chopping boards and brickwork magicked from coffee sacks) and an attention-grabbing red neon sign ensure this diminutive spot stands out.

Of course, when you serve coffee as good as this, commanding attention isn't a problem. The house espresso is Caravan's Daily Blend – a rigorously tested and carefully roasted combo of new-crop beans showcasing notes of dark choc, brown sugar and praline.

TIP CELEBRATE THE CITY'S DISTILLING TRADITION WITH A BRISTOL DRY GIN AND TONIC

Despite the kiosk's tiny footprint, the team also manage to whip up smoothies and snacks. Bagels are a firm customer favourite, with the classic smoked salmon and cream cheese combo leading the pack (veggie and vegan options also feature).

Come nightfall, the focus switches to craft beer from local artisan breweries. With a crowd-pleasing playlist thrown in, 640East knows exactly how to start the party.

ESTABLISHED
2019

KEY ROASTER
Caravan Coffee
Roasters

BREWING METHOD
Espresso,
batch brew

MACHINE
La Marzocco
Linea PB

GRINDER
Mazzer Kold S

OPENING HOURS
Mon-Wed 7am-9pm
Thu 7am-10.30pm
Fri 7am-11pm
Sat 9am-11pm
Sun 9am-9pm
(reduced in winter)

www.640east.co.uk   T: 07704 091928
f @640east   @640east

MAP 79 MOKOKO COFFEE & BAKERY – BRISTOL

2 Gaol Ferry Steps, Wapping Wharf, Bristol, BS1 6WE

There are few things more therapeutic than kneading dough or indulging in creative baking – except maybe watching the bakers at work at Mokoko's Wapping Wharf outpost.

From early doors, this talented team of breadsmiths and pastry pros craft the next batch of sugar-encrusted cruffins, lacquered croissants and flavour-popping cakes. The sunrise starts and dedication to the dough really paid off last year when Mokoko scooped nine Great Taste Awards.

INSIDER'S TIP IN SUMMER, GRAB A SPOT ON THE OUTSIDE SEATING TO SIP UNDER THE SUN

It's not just bakery skills that the team take great pride in, however, as the line-up of seasonal coffees is also homemade: roasted in-house and prepared by baristas passionate about the craft. Single origins from Africa and Central and South America feature regularly and there's also an extended selection on the retail shelves for customers to take home.

Visit mid-morning or late afternoon to miss the lunchtime rush as the help-yourself selection of frittata, quiches and salads makes Mokoko a popular spot with the local workforce of creatives and freelancers.

ESTABLISHED
2016

KEY ROASTER
Mokoko

BREWING METHOD
Espresso,
Kalita Wave,
drip, AeroPress,
batch brew

MACHINE
Conti Monte
Carlo

GRINDER
Compak E10
Master

OPENING HOURS
Mon-Fri **7.30**am-**5.30**pm
Sat **8**am-**6.30**pm
Sun **9**am-**6.30**pm

 Gluten FREE

 BEANS AVAILABLE INSTORE

 WIFI

 CYCLE FRIENDLY

 OUTDOOR seating

 DISABLED ACCESS

 BRING YOUR OWN Cup

 DOG FRIENDLY

www.mokokocoffee.com   **T:** 01179 290177

f @mokokocoffee   @ @mokokocoffee

MAP 80 LITTLE VICTORIES

7 Gaol Ferry Steps, Wapping Wharf, Bristol, BS1 6WE

Little Victories keeps Bristol's harbourside buzzing seven days a week, delivering the goods in the form of early morning flat whites and post-work craft beers.

This sister venue to Small Street Espresso bears little resemblance to the original: the focus on brewing exceptionally good coffee, great service and its sky-blue cups are pretty much the only family traits that founders Chris and John passed on to their second site. Instead of exposed brick and wooden-floored cosiness you'll find bleached-wood tables, high ceilings and a huge custom letterpress menu board.

Across both venues, the team have ramped up their green credentials this year. Seasonal coffees from Clifton (there's a house espresso blend, a guest espresso and two single origin filters for Chemex and cold brew) are now delivered in 4kg reusable tubs which saves thousands of bags from ending up in landfill.

TIP THE NEW TRIPLE CHEESE TOASTIE FEATURES THE GOOD STUFF FROM THE BRISTOL CHEESEMONGER

Also new is the covered (and heated) outside seating area – the perfect spot to sink a few Cold Brew Negronis after dark.

ESTABLISHED
2016

KEY ROASTER
Clifton Coffee
Roasters

BREWING METHOD
Espresso,
Chemex,
cold brew

MACHINE
Black Eagle
Gravimetric

GRINDER
Mythos,
Mahlkonig EK43

OPENING HOURS
Mon **7.30**am-**5**pm
Tue-Wed **7.30**am-**7**pm
Thu-Fri **7.30**am-**10**pm
Sat **9**am-**10**pm
Sun **9**am-**5**pm

 Gluten FREE

 BEANS AVAILABLE INSTORE

 WIFI

 CYCLE FRIENDLY

 OUTDOOR seating

 DISABLED ACCESS

 BRING YOUR OWN Cup

 COFFEE COURSES

---

www.littlevics.co.uk

f @littlevicsbristol 🐦 @littlevicsbris 📷 @littlevicsbris

MAP 81 SWEVEN COFFEE

12 North Street, Bedminster, Bristol, BS3 1HT

Photo: Harrison Dowling

Bristol was the epicentre of the coffee quake that rocked the South West in the 2010s, and its latest opening is a fine example of the kind of dynamic and progressive speciality venue that inspired others to join the industry.

Sweven co-founder Jimmy Dimitrov played a part in shaping the city's coffee scene: the qualified Q grader was head of education at Clifton Coffee for five years (he also placed second in Coffee Masters at The London Coffee Festival 2019).

This industry experience is manifest throughout the cafe and Jimmy and co-founder Aga Dimitrov work closely with producers and roasters to source and brew the highest quality coffee they can get their mitts on. High-spec equipment and a skilled-up team of baristas ensure that beans from Clifton, Crankhouse and Red Bank (among a long list) are prepped to exacting standards.

TIP SAMPLE INTERNATIONAL COFFEES FROM ROASTERIES SUCH AS KOPPI AND SEY

Kondo-style minimalism at the beautifully light and bright space keeps the attention firmly on the coffee. Pair exceptional beans in a V60 with a slice of homemade cake from the geometric bar and find yourself in Sweven heaven.

ESTABLISHED
2019

KEY ROASTER
Clifton Coffee Roasters

BREWING METHOD
Espresso, V60

MACHINE
La Marzocco Modbar

GRINDER
Victoria Arduino Mythos 2

OPENING HOURS
Mon-Fri **8**am-**5**pm
Sat **9**am-**5**pm
Sun **10**am-**4**pm

Gluten FREE

BEANS AVAILABLE INSTORE

WIFI

CYCLE FRIENDLY

BRING YOUR OWN Cup

COFFEE COURSES

DOG FRIENDLY

www.swevencoffee.co.uk   T: 07585 906367

f @swevencoffee   🐦 @swevencoffee   📷 @swevencoffee

MAP№ 82 TINCAN COFFEE CO – NORTH STREET

234 North Street, Bedminster, Bristol, BS3 1JD

Flying the Tincan flag in south Bristol, this funky North Street venue utilises headlamp lighting and truck-based booths to reference Tincan's origins as a mobile coffee venture.

Founders Adam White and Jessie Nicolson turned their passion for speciality coffee and vintage vehicle restoration into a business in 2011 when they started slinging shots on the festival circuit via a restored Citroën truck.

TIP NAB A WINDOW STOOL AND WATCH THE BUSY HUBBUB ON NORTH STREET AS YOU SIP YOUR BREW

The mobile fleet has multiplied since then and Tincan now includes two bricks-and-mortar cafes. Whether visiting the permanent sites or the vans, bean geeks can be confident they'll enjoy a cracking house espresso from Bristol roastery Clifton and that single origin guest roasts will also be available.

The community focus runs through the seasonally changing food offering, too, and Tincan only sources ingredients from local independents. Last year it took an ethical stance against avocados and has replaced them with seasonally changing alternatives such as pea guacamole served on sourdough with poached egg, beetroot and feta.

ESTABLISHED
2016

KEY ROASTER
Clifton Coffee Roasters

BREWING METHOD
Espresso, filter

MACHINE
La Marzocco Linea PB

GRINDER
Mythos One, Compak

OPENING HOURS
Mon-Sat 8am-6pm
Sun 9am-5pm

 Gluten FREE

 BEANS AVAILABLE INSTORE

WIFI

CYCLE FRIENDLY

OUTDOOR seating

BRING YOUR OWN cup.

 DOG FRIENDLY

---

www.tincancoffee.co.uk   T: 01179 633979

f @tincancoffeeco   🐦 @tincancoffeeco   📷 @tincancoffeeco

MAP 83 TINCAN COFFEE TRUCKS

Music festivals and high profile sporting events across the UK

Whenever and wherever the desire for speciality coffee strikes it must be sated – something the team at Tincan understand only too well. That's why the brigade of beautifully refurbished trucks regularly departs from its Bristol base to pitch up at events across the country where revellers are in need of quality caffeination.

The troupe of retro vans – which includes a 1963 Citroën H, 1977 Peugeot J7 and newbie Elliott, a 1978 Renault Estafette – has headlined the coffee offering at festivals such as Goodwood, No. 6 and Latitude, and kept the action rolling on film sets for Sky Atlantic, HBO and the BBC.

TIP: THE UK'S SHORTEST AIRSTREAM HAS RECENTLY JOINED THE TINCAN FLEET

There aren't many mobile venues sporting La Marzocco machines or grinders filled with ethically sourced, speciality-grade beans (in this case roasted in Bristol by Clifton), but the team at Tincan refuse to compromise on quality.

Alongside top-notch espresso they also craft iced drinks, speciality teas, hot choc and cakes to keep party-goers and film crews cranked up to the max.

ESTABLISHED
2011

KEY ROASTER
Clifton Coffee Roasters

BREWING METHOD
Espresso

MACHINE
La Marzocco Linea

GRINDER
Compak E8

Gluten FREE

BEANS AVAILABLE
TINSTORE

CYCLE FRIENDLY

OUTDOOR SEATING

BRING YOUR OWN Cup

DOG FRIENDLY

---

www.tincanevents.co.uk   T: 07725 880581

f @tincanevents   🐦 @tincanevents   📷 @tincanevents

ROASTERY

MAP N° 84 EXTRACT COFFEE ROASTERS

Roastery Works, Unit 1, New Gatton Road, Bristol, BS2 9SH

Since 2007, Extract has had one simple mission: to make coffee better for people and the planet.

The Bristol roastery was instrumental in establishing and developing the speciality scene in the South West, and its pioneering work over the past 13 years has improved the quality of coffee in cafes across the UK.

New hubs in Manchester and London have expanded the Extract brood, and the team's collective ambition to fulfil their goal is stronger than ever, resulting in further innovation.

'MAKE COFFEE BETTER – FOR PEOPLE AND THE PLANET'

Work on a menagerie of vintage roasters (including Betty, pictured) has reduced energy consumption by 60 per cent, while a recycling initiative is transforming used coffee grounds into biofuel. On the community front, Grounds Up – the charity collective supported by Extract – has seen successes such as the Empire Fighting Chance barista-training scheme land three students from deprived backgrounds jobs at Boston Tea Party.

ESTABLISHED
2007

ROASTER
MAKE & SIZE
Probat 120kg
Probat 60kg
Probat 12kg x 2
Ozturk 6kg

OPEN BY APPOINTMENT

COFFEE COURSES

COURSES

BEANS AVAILABLE
ONLINE ONSITE

www.extractcoffee.co.uk   T: 01179 554976

f @extractcoffeeroasters   🐦 @extractcoffee   📷 @extractcoffee

SOMERSET

Nº97
Moo and Two

Portishead

93

85

A4

94 Chew Magna

A39 **BATH** **96**

M5

Weston-super-Mare

A368 Blagdon

97

Mendip Hills AONB

95

Midsomer Norton

Burnham-on-Sea

A371

Frome

Wells Shepton Mallet

Glastonbury

A359

M5

A37

A303

98

A303

Sherborne

Yeovil

A37

CAFES

85 8e Chelsea Road
93 Mokoko Coffee & Bakery – Portishead
94 Yeo Valley Canteen
95 Strangers with Coffee
96 The River House
97 Moo and Two
98 Finca

*All locations are approximate

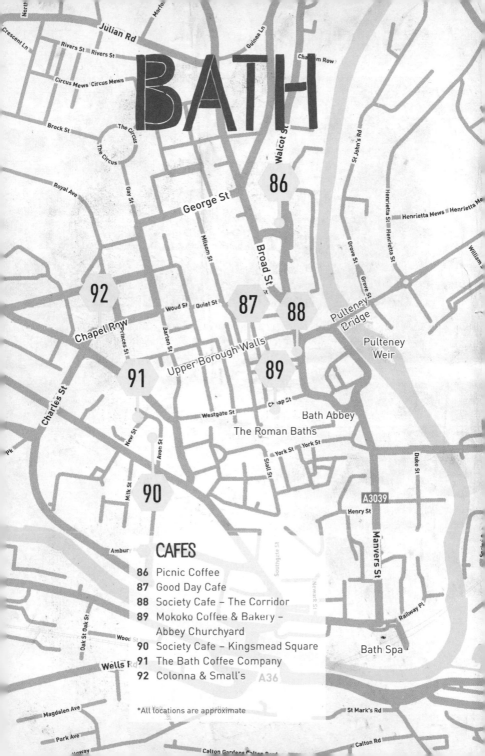

BATH

CAFES

86 Picnic Coffee
87 Good Day Cafe
88 Society Cafe – The Corridor
89 Mokoko Coffee & Bakery –
   Abbey Churchyard
90 Society Cafe – Kingsmead Square
91 The Bath Coffee Company
92 Colonna & Small's

*All locations are approximate

MAP No. 85 8E CHELSEA ROAD

8e Chelsea Road, Bath, BA1 3DU

The team at 8e revel in curating all of their favourite things – from coffee to food and booze – in one place. So be prepared to find Wiltshire haslet and Larkhall plums rubbing shoulders with Colombian beans and local craft beers at this Bath indie.

The team are just as passionate about creating an exceptional customer experience, whether that's pulling the perfect morning espresso, crafting wholesome lunch plates or providing an epic range of craft beers for post-work revelry.

Food and drink is driven by the seasons here and 8e's enormous windows mean the weather outside dictates the vibe within. In winter darkness, for instance, soft lights glitter amid a collection of plants, creating an ideal atmosphere for an amorous evening spent sharing a bottle of full-bodied red.

INSIDERS' TIP: CHECK OUT THE STUNNING FLOOR WHICH REVEALS LAYERS OF COLOUR AND STONES FROM TIMES GONE BY

If you're sticking to coffee you're in safe hands as these guys have nerd-level knowledge. Beans for the La Marzocco machine and filter kit are roasted at Extract in Bristol, and there's also a roll call of guest roasts worth investigating.

ESTABLISHED
2008

KEY ROASTER
Extract Coffee Roasters

BREWING METHOD
Espresso, filter, AeroPress, cold brew, pourover

MACHINE
La Marzocco Linea PB

GRINDER
Sanremo SR70

OPENING HOURS
Mon-Wed 8am-6pm
Thu-Fri 8am-10pm
Sat 8am-5pm
Sun 9am-4pm

WIFI

CYCLE FRIENDLY

OUTDOOR SEATING

DOG FRIENDLY

№86 PICNIC COFFEE

9 Saracen Street, Bath, BA1 5BR

It's no wonder Picnic Coffee has become an essential stop-off on any day trip in Bath. Situated among the Roman city's vintage and indie stores, the speciality coffee shop is a friendly spot in which to savour a handcrafted brew with a sarnie or locally made bake.

Local roastery Round Hill shares top billing with Staffordshire's Hasbean, while a selection of guest coffees further showcase owner Tim Starks' passion for the good stuff.

The coffee is joined by ethically sourced goodies including loose-leaf infusions from Bristol's Canton Tea, and Bath-made finds such as Heyday Maté caffeinated soda, Bath Culture House kombucha, Henny & Joe's masala chai and Farside cold brew.

TIP VISITORS PICKING UP A TAKEAWAY DRINK SCORE A DISCOUNT IF THEY TAKE ALONG A REUSABLE CUP

It's a beautifully bright and accessible space where wheelchair users, cyclists and canine friends are all welcome. Pups, however, must be willing to pose for a #PicnicProfile on the cafe's Instagram grid – human regulars occasionally make the cut, too.

ESTABLISHED
2013

KEY ROASTER
Multiple roasters

BREWING METHOD
Espresso, V60, AeroPress

MACHINE
Victoria Arduino Black Eagle

GRINDER
Victoria Arduino Mythos One, Mahlkonig EK43, Mahlkonig K30

OPENING HOURS
Mon-Fri **7.30**am-**6**pm
Sat **8.30**am-**6**pm
Sun **9**am-**6**pm

WIFI

---

www.picniccoffee.co.uk   T: 01225 330128

f @picniccoffee   🐦 @picnic_bath   📷 @picnic_bath

MAP 87 GOOD DAY CAFE

12 Upper Borough Walls, Bath, BA1 1RH

Next time you need a coffee-and-cake mood booster in Bath, think pink.

A trip to this rosy-hued hangout, just off the city's tourist trail, is guaranteed to remedy any mid-morning slump or late-afternoon brain fuzz. The coffee's on-point, positivity oozes from the friendly staff and there's even a doggy wall of fame if pictures of cute pups are the quickest route to your endorphin reserves.

INSIDER TIP: SPREAD THE LOVE: LEAVE A MESSAGE ON THE POSITIVITY WALL

An early morning shot of the Good Day house coffee – expertly roasted in Scotland by the bean geeks at Unorthodox – lives up to its name. The mellow caramel and hazelnut notes of the Brazilian single origin simultaneously soothe the soul and awaken the senses when laced with Estate Dairy milk from Chew Valley.

If you've got time to stick around, order from a menu that reads like a who's who of Bath's fabulous food indies: cakes from Homemade by Ella, craft wine via Wolf Wine and stroopwaffles made by Dutch Boy, plus sourdough from Pistrina in Bristol.

ESTABLISHED
2018

KEY ROASTER
Unorthodox
Roasters

BREWING METHOD
Espresso, V60

MACHINE
La Marzocco
Linea PB

GRINDER
Mazzer
Major x 2

OPENING HOURS
Mon-Fri **8**am-**5**pm
Sat **9**am-**6**pm
Sun **10**am-**4**pm

 Gluten FREE

 BEANS AVAILABLE INSTORE

 WIFI

 OUTDOOR seating

BRING YOUR OWN Cup

 DOG FRIENDLY

www.gooddaycoffee.co.uk   T: 01225 684284

f @gooddaycafebath   @gooddaycafe

MAP №88 SOCIETY CAFE – THE CORRIDOR

19 High Street, Bath, BA1 5AJ

Located at the entrance of Bath's famous indoor arcade, this pint-sized version of Society's original Kingsmead Square venue provides a dose of caffeinated respite for weary shoppers. It's also a buzzy takeout spot for day-trippers.

City stompers grab a coffee to-go, but those seeking a slower sip are usually found sitting at the window bar or outdoor tables which offer views over the Abbey and the Guildhall. If the first floor is overflowing there's also additional seating in the pared-back basement.

TIP THUMB THROUGH A COPY OF SOCIETY'S IN-HOUSE NEWSPAPER FOR ART AND CAFFEINE INSPO

Society's house espresso is the result of a long relationship with Cornish roastery Origin and it shifts in terms of terroir and tasting notes, depending on the seasonal global coffee harvests.

A guest list chock-full of thoughtfully sourced beans from the UK and beyond provides plenty of alt options – recently featured roasters include Round Hill, Berlin's The Barn and down-the-road pals Colonna.

Whether you're staying or going, be sure to pair your brew with one of the tempting bakes which line the counter.

ESTABLISHED
2014

KEY ROASTER
Origin Coffee
Roasters

BREWING METHOD
Espresso,
AeroPress,
cold brew,
batch brew

MACHINE
La Marzocco
Linea PB

GRINDER
Mahlkonig
Tanzania,
Mahlkonig EK43,
Nuova Simonelli
Mythos x 2

OPENING HOURS
Mon-Sat 7.30am-6.30pm
Sun 9am-6pm

 Gluten FREE

 BEANS AVAILABLE / INSTORE

 WIFI

 CYCLE FRIENDLY

 OUTDOOR seating

 DISABLED ACCESS

 BRING YOUR OWN cup

 DOG FRIENDLY

---

www.society-cafe.com T: 01225 428008

f @societycafebath 🐦 @societycafe 📷 @societycafe

MAP № 89 MOKOKO COFFEE & BAKERY – ABBEY CHURCHYARD

6 Abbey Churchyard, Bath, BA1 1LY

Georgian architecture, sweeping crescents, Roman baths and Jane Austen grandeur are head-turners that attract tourists by the bus-load to Bath. Visitors looking to escape the busy streets, however, will be thankful to know of a coffee shop with great views, an enticing array of speciality coffees and shelves laden with edible delights.

Its coffee, served by a lively team who aren't snobby about the "right way" to drink it, is crafted from house-roasted beans. Favour a long black over a cortado? You got it. Prefer rich dark notes to floral fragrance? No problem. Espresso over V60? The team will tailor it to your taste.

TIP DESIGNS ON THE MOKOKO COFFEE BAGS REFERENCE THE CULTURE OF THE COUNTRY OF ORIGIN

The drinks menu is fortified by guest roasts from Ross-on-Wye's James Gourmet, as well as a range of loose-leaf infusions served in Japanese-style teapots.

Freshly baked foccacia and bagels restore sightseeing stamina while still leaving space for temptations (crafted at the sister bakery in Bristol) such as beautifully laminated pastries made with Lescure butter and Shipton Mill flour.

ESTABLISHED
2011

KEY ROASTER
Mokoko

BREWING METHOD
Espresso,
Clever Dripper,
AeroPress, V60

MACHINE
Conti Monte
Carlo

GRINDER
Compak E8,
Compak E10

OPENING HOURS
Wed-Sat 8am-6pm
Sun 9am-6pm

 Gluten FREE

 BEANS AVAILABLE INSTORE

 WIFI

 CYCLE FRIENDLY

 OUTDOOR SEATING

 BRING YOUR OWN CUP

 DOG FRIENDLY

---

www.mokokocoffee.com   T: 01225 758132

f @mokokocoffee   @ @mokokocoffee

MAP№90 SOCIETY CAFE – KINGSMEAD SQUARE

5 Kingsmead Square, Bath, BA1 2AB

The flagship venue in Society's quartet of cafes is a welcome-to-all hub which provides gratification for everyone who steps through its bright blue doorway.

Coffee snobs will find their thirst sated via the evolving selection of beans: Cornwall's Origin supplies a new house roast each season, while roasters from across Europe take turns in the weekly changing guest slot. Espresso and filter options keep things fresh and novel.

Those with a passion for provenance find fulfilment through locally sourced produce: fresh milk is delivered daily from Frome's Ivy House Farm; sarnies are stuffed with ingredients from indie producers; and loose-leaf teas are supplied by fellow Bathonians Teahouse Emporium.

☞TIP WILLIE'S CACAO AND KOKOA COLLECTION HOT CHOCS CALL FOR A FURTHER VISIT – OR A SECOND CUP

Coffee and food sustenance is supplemented by fuel for the soul: a creative space for children to explore; art house mags for grown-ups to browse; exhibitions; and, occasionally, an artist in residence. The crew have even launched their own Society newspaper for customers to flick through while they sip.

ESTABLISHED
2012

KEY ROASTER
Origin Coffee
Roasters

BREWING METHOD
Espresso,
AeroPress,
cold brew,
batch brew

MACHINE
La Marzocco
Linea PB

GRINDER
Mahlkonig K30,
Mahlkonig
Tanzania,
Nuova Simonelli
Mythos

OPENING HOURS
Mon-Fri **7**am-**6.30**pm
Sat **7.30**am-**6.30**pm
Sun **9**am-**6**pm

 Gluten FREE

 BEANS AVAILABLE INSTORE

 WIFI

 CYCLE FRIENDLY

 OUTDOOR Seating

 DISABLED ACCESS

 BRING YOUR OWN Cup

 DOG FRIENDLY

www.society-cafe.com T: 01225 442433
f @societycafebath 🐦 @societycafe 📷 @societycafe

ᴹᴬᴾ №91 THE BATH COFFEE COMPANY

14 Kingsmead Square, Bath, BA1 2AD

Adrian Smith, founder of The Bath Coffee Company, has absolute confidence in the quality of the beans in every cup served at his Kingsmead Square coffee house. It's well founded: he's the one who bronzes the beans at Wiltshire roastery Square Root Coffee.

The cafe's signature blend The Solution (a marriage of Brazilian, Sumatran and Indian lots) has been fine-tuned to yield crowd-pleasing chocolatey notes and a smooth mouthfeel.

ᴵᴺˢᴵᴰᴱᴿˢ TIP PROMISCUOUS SIPPER? ORDER A SAMPLE PACK FROM THE SQUARE ROOT WEBSITE

Sample it as a flat white and pair it with one of the delish cakes and pastries from the countertop collection. And, if you're hanging out with friends, get stuck in to the stash of board games while trying one of the single origins prepared as AeroPress or V60.

The friendly welcome and fine coffee to be found at this central spot have garnered such a fanbase that Adrian and team have created a photo wall featuring the faces and coffee orders of over 200 regulars. The creative installation takes 'getting to know the locals' to a whole new level.

ESTABLISHED
2014

KEY ROASTER
Square Root Coffee

BREWING METHOD
Espresso, V60, AeroPress

MACHINE
La Pavoni

GRINDER
La Pavoni, Cunill, Mazzer

OPENING HOURS
Mon-Sun **8**am-**6**pm

WIFI

CYCLE
FRIENDLY

OUTDOOR
seating

BRING
YOUR OWN
cup.

DOG
FRIENDLY

---

www.bathcoffeecompany.co.uk   T: 07940 120835

f @thebathcoffeeco   @bathcoffeecompany

MAP№ 92 COLONNA & SMALL'S

6 Chapel Row, Bath, BA1 1HN

This Bath coffee shop should be on the hit-list of every adventurous bean fiend. Not only did it win Best Coffee Shop in Europe in 2016 (Allegra European Coffee Awards), it's also the base of multi-award-winning barista and all-round grind guru Maxwell Colonna-Dashwood.

Visit the contemporary cafe to delight your palate with rare and unusual coffees. They're served with precision by a talented team who are extremely knowledgeable about the beans and the best way to prep them.

TIP TRY COLONNA'S LUNGO WHICH SITS SOMEWHERE BETWEEN AN ESPRESSO AND A DELICATE FILTER

It's not surprising that the baristas are all over the background of the beans as, in recent years, Maxwell has moved from merely crafting coffee to also roasting it. Currently the team are excited about the first crop from Gorongosa mountain in Mozambique, a special coffee that has yet to be showcased in the UK. 'There isn't much of it as production is very small, but we're working with the Gorongosa Project to help bring this new and special origin to light,' says Maxwell.

Three different espressos and filters feature on the board and change every few days in celebration of coffee's infinite variety.

ESTABLISHED
2009

KEY ROASTER
Colonna Coffee Roasters

BREWING METHOD
Espresso, AeroPress, syphon

MACHINE
Modbar

GRINDER
Mahlkonig EK43

OPENING HOURS
Mon-Fri 8am-5.30pm
Sat 8.30am-5.30pm
Sun 10am-4pm

 Gluten FREE

 BEANS AVAILABLE INSTORE

 WIFI

 CYCLE FRIENDLY

 OUTDOOR SEATING

 BRING YOUR OWN Cup.

 DOG FRIENDLY

www.colonnaandsmalls.co.uk   T: 07766 808067

f @colonnacoffee 🐦 @colonna_smalls 📷 @colonnacoffee

MAP №93 MOKOKO COFFEE & BAKERY – PORTISHEAD

313 Newfoundland Way, The Marina, Portishead, Somerset, BS20 7QH

The Mokoko team are ever extending their coffee and bakery concept and have recently embarked on their most ambitious project yet.

Residing in a roomy spot on Portishead's scenic marina, the new cafe (the largest of four outposts) mirrors the Wapping Wharf set-up with communal seating around an open-plan bakery and coffee bar. Huge floor-to-ceiling windows flood the space with light, emphasising the kaleidoscopic colour scheme inside.

TIP PICK UP A FRESHLY BAKED LOAF OF SOURDOUGH WITH YOUR FLAT WHITE

Almost everything on the menu is made in-house – which extends to the Mokoko beans filling the Compak grinders. The team have also collaborated with the roasters at James Gourmet in Herefordshire on a seasonal collection of single origins and blends.

Arrive hungry so you can feast on mushroom and wheat berry filo parcels with your flat white. Follow with a house hero such as the cruffin filled with clementine cream, white chocolate and honeycomb, plus one of the latest lots via Clever Dripper.

ESTABLISHED
2019

KEY ROASTER
Mokoko

BREWING METHOD
Espresso,
Clever Dripper

MACHINE
Conti Monte
Carlo

GRINDER
Compak PKE,
Compak PK100

OPENING HOURS
Mon-Sun
8am-5.30pm

Gluten FREE

BEANS AVAILABLE
INSTORE

WIFI

CYCLE FRIENDLY

OUTDOOR seating

DISABLED ACCESS

BRING YOUR OWN cup

DOG FRIENDLY

---

www.mokokocoffee.com   T: 01275 845620

f @mokokocoffee   @ @mokokocoffee

MAP 94 YEO VALLEY CANTEEN

Yeo Valley HQ, Blagdon, Somerset, BS40 7YE

Most can only dream of having a staff canteen like Yeo Valley's but, thankfully, the milk maestros have been kind enough to share it with external visitors.

The Blagdon HQ has long held a reputation for its cracking fodder, stonking valley views and top-notch caffeine and, in 2015, the team decided to welcome the wider public into the quirkily designed spot so that they too could enjoy a bite of the action.

TIP NEW OPENING HOURS MEAN BREKKIE IS NOW AN OPTION, TOO. HELLO SMOKED HADDOCK KEDGEREE

Now, day-trippers and speciality seekers share the space with the dairy's workforce as they sip velvety flat whites crafted from Yeo Valley milk and beans roasted by Bristol's Extract.

Of course, a visit isn't complete without trying the award-bagging foodie offering. Only the best organic British produce is used in this kitchen and staff faves like the Holt Farm beef burger with Green's organic cheddar live up to the standard of the brews.

Another benefit of a visit is the wall of fridges stocked with Yeo Valley milk, yogurt and butter which can be snapped up at a decent discount.

ESTABLISHED
2015

KEY ROASTER
Extract Coffee Roasters

BREWING METHOD
Espresso

MACHINE
La Spaziale

GRINDER
Mazzer

OPENING HOURS
Tue-Fri **8.30**am **5**pm

Gluten FREE

WIFI

OUTDOOR Seating

DISABLED ACCESS

BRING YOUR OWN Cup

---

www.yeovalley.co.uk   **T:** 01761 258155

f @yeovalley   🐦 @yeovalley   📷 @yeovalley

MAP №95 STRANGERS WITH COFFEE

31 St Cuthbert Street, Wells, Somerset, BA5 2AW

Once you've had your fill of boutique shops and ancient buildings in the tiny cathedral city of Wells, you'll be ready to throw yourself on the kindness of strangers at this Somerset stalwart.

Speciality fans arrive at Strangers with Coffee as customers but tend to leave as friends. Bean buffs enjoy a warm rapport with co-owner and barista Tom Lowe, who offers a coffee menu diverse in both its origins and flavour profiles. Bonding takes place over a spectrum of beans from around the globe.

Allpress Espresso is Tom's tasty mainstay, but ever-changing guest coffees ensure he always has something additional brewing. Behind the scenes, co-owner Jerry Naish looks after the classic coffee shop food offering.

TIP MANDI'S MASSIVE BISCOFF CAKE IS LEGENDARY

Fuel your day with the Strangers special breakfast: thick crusty bread topped with beans, a poached egg, chorizo and a sprinkling of chilli flakes. Or, on summer days, head to the courtyard to pair a cold-brew soda with a slice of cake from the beauty parade on the counter.

ESTABLISHED
2012

KEY ROASTER
Allpress Espresso

BREWING METHOD
Espresso, V60

MACHINE
La Marzocco Linea

GRINDER
Mythos One, Mahlkonig Vario, Mazzer Super Jolly

OPENING HOURS
Tue-Sat **7.30**am-**4**pm

Gluten FREE

BEANS AVAILABLE
INSTORE

OUTDOOR seating

BRING YOUR OWN cup

DOG FRIENDLY

T: 07729 226200

f @strangerswithcoffee   @strangerscoffeewells

MAP № 96 THE RIVER HOUSE

7 The Bridge, Frome, Somerset, BA11 1AR

The gang at this Frome coffee house describe themselves as *'a small gaggle of coffee-loving, breakfast-boshing, brunch-eating, lunch-craving, cocktail-making, beer-drinking, gin-sinking cafe fanatics'.*

To say the team are enterprising about having a bloomin' good time is something of an understatement. Recent antics have included a Mime Day (a whole Friday service delivered in silence, with communication only via gestures), an American Diner Day (with mississippi mud pie shakes) and fundraising events including a baring-all calendar in aid of Mind and Somerset & Wessex Eating Disorders Association.

TIP REFILL OLD COFFEE BAGS WITH WHOLE OR GROUND BEANS TO BREW AT HOME

While a day behind the funky bar at The River House is clearly a lot of LOLs, the squad take the coffee pretty seriously and roast the house blend Proper Gobby at their Loud Mouth roastery. Guest slots are filled by Hilperton roaster Dusty Ape and there's always a decaf on the go for those who crave *'flavour without crazy behaviour'.*

The food's fun, too: weekly brunch specials sit alongside egg-based regulars such as NamEggStay and Papa-Rosti.

ESTABLISHED
2014

KEY ROASTER
Loud Mouth
Coffee

BREWING METHOD
Espresso, filter,
cold brew

MACHINE
Astoria Plus

GRINDER
La Cimbali
Magnum

OPENING HOURS
Mon-Fri
8.30am-**5.30**pm
Sat **9**am-**6**pm
Sun **10**am-**4**pm

Gluten FREE

BEANS AVAILABLE INSTORE

WIFI

CYCLE FRIENDLY

OUTDOOR seating

DISABLED ACCESS

BRING YOUR OWN Cup

DOG FRIENDLY

www.riverhousefrome.co.uk   T: 07963 394391

f @theriverhousefrome   🐦 @riverhousefrome   📷 @riverhousefrome

MAP№ 97 MOO AND TWO

27 Catherine Hill, Frome, Somerset, BA11 1BY

Everything tastes better when sipped in a beautiful environment – and beauty is in abundance at Moo and Two.

For a start, stunning handmade ceramic "Fi60s" – crafted by Frome potter Fi Underhill – give pourover fans more than just their drip brew to lust over. Batch brew and Chemex make up the trio of clean-as-a-whistle filter options through which visitors can explore a new collab between Moo and Somerset roaster Round Hill.

Take your pick of the coffee offering while perched on one of the wooden benches lining the exposed-brick walls, then admire the plant-peppered decor as you tuck in to a locally made pastry.

TIP CHOOSE A TUNE FROM THE VINYL COLLECTION AND GIVE IT A SPIN

Saving the planet is high on the agenda and the Moo herd have embraced everything compostable and recyclable. They run a cup-loan scheme for locals and were recently named as one of Frome's Plastic Free Champions.

They're also hot on tea, so it's worth returning to switch up the piccolo for pekoe. Drop by for one of the music and cocktail evenings, too.

ESTABLISHED
2016

KEY ROASTER
Round Hill
Roastery

BREWING METHOD
Espresso,
pourover,
batch brew,
Chemex

MACHINE
La Spaziale S5

GRINDER
Mythos

OPENING HOURS
Tue-Sat **9**am-**5**pm
Sun **9.30**am-**3**pm

Gluten FREE

BEANS AVAILABLE
INSTORE

WIFI

CYCLE FRIENDLY

OUTDOOR seating

BRING YOUR OWN cup.

DOG FRIENDLY

---

www.mooandtwo.com T: 07816 311452

f @mooandtwo 🐦 @mooandtwo 📷 @mooandtwo

MAP № 98 FINCA – YEOVIL

11 High Street, Yeovil, Somerset, BA20 1RG

When you need speciality refreshment and a break from the bustle of Yeovil town centre, head to Finca and unwind within its welcoming rustic-wood and bare-brick interior. On summer days, the bi-fold doors are drawn back and customers gravitate towards the sun-soaked tables outside.

Finca's quartet of coffee shops are like satellites revolving around the Dorchester HQ where the roasting takes place in a 10kg Toper. Beans from farms in Rwanda, Colombia and up-and-coming regions such as East Timor are carefully bronzed by founder Don Iszatt before they're dispatched to the family of hoppers at the cafes.

TIP SEASONALITY IS KING AT FINCA, SO LOOK OUT FOR NEW ROASTS THROUGHOUT THE YEAR

A La Marzocco Linea – under the guidance of expert baristas – performs espresso duties at the Yeovil outpost. However, if you're up for a clean filter experience you'll also find single origins to explore via V60 and cold brew.

Just the right kind of food is on hand to perfectly pair with your caffeine hit: oozing traybakes, flaky pastries and indulgent cakes are freshly made each day at Finca's Poundbury bakery.

ESTABLISHED
2016

KEY ROASTER
Finca Coffee Roasters

BREWING METHOD
Espresso, V60, cold brew

MACHINE
La Marzocco Linea

GRINDER
Olympus

OPENING HOURS
Mon-Sat 8am-4pm
Sun 10am-2pm

Gluten FREE

BEANS AVAILABLE INSTORE

OUTDOOR SEATING

BRING YOUR OWN Cup

DOG FRIENDLY

---

www.fincacoffee.co.uk   T: 01305 300400

f @fincayeovil   🐦 @scouting4coffee   📷 @scouting4coffee

DEVON

Nº109
The Other Cup

CAFES

⬢ ROASTERIES

*All locations are approximate

MAP № 99 ANNIE AND THE FLINT

125-126 High Street, Ilfracombe, Devon, EX34 9EY

This seaside speciality spot is bucking the trend for ice creams and fish and chips in Ilfracombe and has instead garnered a following for its cakes, healthy snacks and vegan/veggie leanings.

The increasing demand for its homemade pizzas, sarnies and salad bowls – coupled with a reliable menu of coffee, smoothies and juices – has even necessitated expansion into the space next door.

Take your pick of espresso-based coffees made with beans roasted in Cornwall by Origin, then surrender yourself to the cult of cake-ism. Confections like sesame snap blondies and jaffa brownies inspire loyal devotion.

TIP FIRST CUSTOMER OF THE DAY TO CLAP EYES ON THE ITINERANT TOBY JUG WINS A FREE COFFEE

Brekkies span the range from homemade granola to pancakes with compote, yogurt and berries, and banana bread dripping with cinnamon butter. Everything on the A&F menu is sourced from environmentally friendly and, wherever possible, local suppliers, including the popular kids' lunchboxes.

ESTABLISHED
2016

KEY ROASTER
Origin Coffee Roasters

BREWING METHOD
Espresso

MACHINE
La Marzocco

GRINDER
Mythos One

OPENING HOURS
Mon-Fri 8.30am-4.30pm
Sat 9.30am-4pm

 Gluten FREE

 BEANS AVAILABLE INSTORE

 WIFI

 BRING YOUR OWN Cup

---

www.annieandtheflint.co.uk   T: 01271 866436

f @annieandtheflint   @ @annieandtheflint

MAP№ 100 MERAKI COFFEE CO.

12 South Street, Woolacombe, Devon, EX34 7BB

The casual coastal decor and friendly vibe make this Woolacombe venue a fave with both seasoned surfers and discerning visitors who are happy to venture off the main drag in search of good coffee.

Salty-haired swimmers, sandy-toed children and pooped pooch-walkers all take the short stroll from the shore to Meraki to curl their fingers around warming flat whites, refuel with chunky slices of homemade cake and snaffle treats by the roaring log burner.

For coffee fans, there's a crowd-pleasing house blend from local roastery Devon Coffee as well as a guest espresso. Co-founder Anthony Merret likes to switch up the second option every week or so and chooses beans that have caught his attention. Mini visitors can mimic the grown-ups with creamy hot chocs.

INSIDERS TIP NAB A SPOT ON THE SOFA AND GET STUCK IN TO SOME LOCAL LITERATURE

Make time to stop for breakfast or lunch as the little kitchen is always rustling up something delicious. The short menu changes regularly but there's usually a berry-garnished granola bowl or egg-and-avo combo to feed a day of outdoor pursuits.

ESTABLISHED
2018

KEY ROASTER
Devon Coffee
Company

BREWING METHOD
Espresso

MACHINE
Astoria Storm

GRINDER
Fiorenzato F38,
Fiorenzato F83
E EGi,
Anfim Pratica

OPENING HOURS
Mon-Sun 8am-4.30pm

Gluten FREE

BEANS AVAILABLE
INSTORE

WIFI

OUTDOOR seating

DISABLED ACCESS

BRING YOUR OWN Cup

COFFEE COURSES

DOG FRIENDLY

T: 01271 871084
f @merakicoffeeco @merakicoffeecompany

MAP 101 HEARTBREAK HOTEL COFFEE

Unit 4, West Cross, Caen Street, Braunton, Devon, EX33 1AQ

Coffee and cake may not mend a broken heart, but at north Devon's latest speciality hangout they do offer pretty decent consolation.

Heartbreak Hotel started life as a horsebox serving coffee to the surfers of Woolacombe before finding a permanent home in Braunton in 2019. At the new hub, siblings Joe and Ella have introduced a laid-back, Californian-style aesthetic – think minimal design, plywood benches and thrift-shop mugs.

INSIDER TIP VISIT THE ORIGINAL HORSEBOX COFFEE STOP AT WOOLACOMBE FROM EASTER TO SEPTEMBER

The duo spent time in Melbourne and were so inspired by the southern hemisphere's independent coffee scene that they decided to recreate the experience at home with NZ-founded Allpress Espresso and Instagram-friendly interiors.

However, it's not just the caffeine or the decor that have garnered this heartthrob a following: occasional cocktail evenings showcasing concoctions such as 'He's not that (g)in to you' (gin, grapefruit, rosemary) and 'Case of the ex-presso' (vodka, espresso, Kahlua) are a definite draw. The homemade doughnuts are guaranteed to have you weeping (with joy), too.

ESTABLISHED
2017

KEY ROASTER
Allpress Espresso

BREWING METHOD
Espresso, V60, AeroPress

MACHINE
La Marzocco

GRINDER
Mazzer Major Electronic

OPENING HOURS
Mon-Wed, Fri
8am-4pm
Sat-Sun 9am-4pm

 Gluten FREE
 BEANS AVAILABLE INSTORE
 WIFI
 OUTDOOR seating
 BRING YOUR OWN cup
DOG FRIENDLY

---

www.heartbreakhotelcoffee.com   T: 07986 709630
f @heartbreakhotelcoffee 🐦 @heahocoffee 📷 @heartbreakhotelcoffee

MAP№ 102 51 DEGREES NORTH COFFEE COMPANY

Unit 6, Velator Way, Braunton, Devon, EX33 2FB

Keeping festivalgoers full of beans – without the use of plastic – is Justin Duerden's mission, and one he's undertaking using an extraordinary solar-powered van complete with mobile brew bar.

Not content with simply offering a range of on-the-go espresso-based drinks, Justin also serves up a mean single origin pourover to coffee lovers across the county.

TIP CATCH THE VAN WEEKDAY MORNINGS OUTSIDE TESCO IN BRAUNTON

Each coffee is crafted from beans roasted at Devon's Coffee Factory and Justin says: *'Despite the challenges of being outdoors all year round, we consistently pour high quality coffee which is measured and made with precision'*.

In addition, 51 Degrees North is probably one of the first – if not *the* first – mobile coffee businesses to utilise hydrogen-rich antioxidant water in each brew.

Milk is sourced from a local farm and collected in reusable jerry cans, while Devon-blended organic tea leaves and real hot chocolate mean it's not just coffee drinkers who get to enjoy a stonkingly good sip.

ESTABLISHED
2017

KEY ROASTER
Coffee Factory

BREWING METHOD
Espresso,
Clever Dripper,
AeroPress,
cold brew

MACHINE
Astoria

GRINDER
Anfim Scody II,
Baratza Sette 270,
Wilfa Svart

OPENING HOURS
Mon-Fri from **8**am
Sat-Sun as per event

 Gluten FREE

 BEANS AVAILABLE INSTORE

 CYCLE FRIENDLY

 OUTDOOR SEATING

 DISABLED & ACCESS

 BRING YOUR OWN CUP

 COFFEE COURSES

 DOG FRIENDLY

---

www.51degreesnorthcoffee.com   **T:** 07403 944544

f @51degreesnorthcoffee   🐦 @51degnorthcc   📷 @51degreesnorthcoffee

MAP 103 BLOCK

12-14 Butchers Row, Barnstaple, Devon, EX31 1BW

For top-notch coffee and contemporary street food, you'd be hard pressed to beat this slice of urban cool sandwiched among the indie stores and cafes of Barnstaple's Butchers Row.

The ever-changing menu is a globetrotting affair: huevos rancheros and sky-high American-style pancakes rub shoulders with bacon butties at breakfast. Then, come lunch, a line-up of fresh and healthy midday dishes takes inspiration from the East. Hard-to-fake favourites like ramen, pho and katsu curry are crafted with authenticity and care.

INSIDER'S TIP
LOOK OUT FOR THE EVENING SUPPER CLUBS WHICH SHOWCASE STREET FOOD FROM AROUND THE WORLD

Fantastic food is only half the story: you'd be mad to miss out on a glossy Clifton Coffee flat white served in a vintage pottery cup. Sip at your leisure while soaking up the lively bustle.

If you're watching your carbon footprint you can put your feet up at Block. Since day one, founders Tran and Andy Stephenson have worked to keep their impact on the planet to a minimum, from bulk-buying recyclable packaging to minimising food waste.

ESTABLISHED
2017

KEY ROASTER
Clifton Coffee Roasters

BREWING METHOD
Espresso

MACHINE
La Marzocco

GRINDER
Compak

OPENING HOURS
Tue-Sat 8am-5pm

Gluten FREE

BEANS AVAILABLE INSTORE

WIFI

DISABLED ACCESS

BRING YOUR OWN Cup

DOG FRIENDLY

---

www.eatatblock.com   **T:** 01271 342045

f @eatatblock   🐦 @eatatblock   📷 @eatatblock

MAP 104 BEATSWORKIN

9 Queens House, Queens Street, Barnstaple, Devon, EX32 8HJ

The team at Beatsworkin manage to squeeze a helluva lot into their independent north Devon shrine to skate and coffee culture.

Owner Glenn Field has created a cafe and skate store in a small space which has become a one-stop shop for skateboard gear, streetwear and a great cup of coffee.

Whether you're a seasoned pro or boarding beginner you'll be welcomed by the Beatsworkin team who excel in fixing carefully crafted coffees. The caffeinated collection is also accompanied by smoothies, milkshakes and a range of locally made bakes.

TIP PERUSE THE STREETWEAR AND SKATE GEAR WHILE YOU WAIT FOR YOUR BREW

While there are no inside tables, there is alfresco seating out front where you can sip your Beanberry Chemex brew and watch the world go by. If you're planning on picking up a flat white to-go don't forget to take your KeepCup along.

As the barista pulls your 'spro on the Sanremo machine, take a moment to check out the array of brew kit and small-batch Beanberry coffee in the retail section – and maybe even cop a skate tee, too.

ESTABLISHED
2015

KEY ROASTER
Beanberry
Coffee Company

BREWING METHOD
Espresso,
Chemex, V60

MACHINE
Sanremo
Verona TCS

GRINDER
Mahlkonig
K30 Air

OPENING HOURS
Tue-Thu 9.30am-5.30pm
Fri-Sat 10am-5.30pm

BEANS AVAILABLE INSTORE

WIFI

OUTDOOR SEATING

BRING YOUR OWN Cup

DOG FRIENDLY

---

www.beatsworkin.net T: 01271 321111

f @beatsworkinuk @beatsworkin

DEVELOPED WITH BARISTAS FOR BARISTAS

- Perfect for latte art
- No added sugar
- Cholesterol free, low fat alternative to milk
- 30% less calories than skimmed & regular soy milk

UNSWEETENED

BLUE DIAMOND ALMONDS

Almond Breeze®

Serving Suggestion

Rich & Creamy

BARISTA BLEND
Created for Use by Professionals
Dairy and Soya Free

Baristas know their coffee better than anyone. That's why we got baristas to help us make our new, low calorie Almond Breeze® Barista Blend. It's deliciously creamy and frothy, making it perfect for the world's finest coffee. And because it's an almond drink, it's dairy free and soya free

For more information & stockists visit **bluediamondalmonds.co.uk**

MAP 105 THE GLASSHOUSE CAFE

Culm Valley Health Centre, Willand Road, Cullompton, Devon, EX15 1FE

Speciality coffee served in a health centre? It may be unusual, yet this family-run cafe is in perfect harmony with its setting thanks to its nutritious menu and wellbeing-enhancing coffee.

Feel the benefits of good nourishment from the Mediterranean-inspired panini, bagels and salads which feature cherry tomatoes, black olives, capers, feta and sundried tomatoes marinated in lemon juice. A herb of the month is also used in a selection of the cafe's lunches, bakes and drinks with the aim of educating patrons about its health-boosting properties.

Coffee from Origin also delivers a feelgood glow. The Cornish roaster is Glasshouse's mainstay for espresso drinks and switches up the beans each month, while in summer visitors can cool off with a cold brew from nearby roastery Roastworks.

INSIDER'S TIP
GLASSHOUSE IS ONE OF THE ONLY CAFES IN THE AREA TO SERVE SPECIALITY COFFEE

Good vibes are guaranteed for both body and spirit as the cafe also hosts social groups which meet weekly to help combat loneliness.

ESTABLISHED
2017

KEY ROASTER
Origin Coffee
Roasters

BREWING METHOD
Espresso,
cold brew

MACHINE
La Marzocco
Linea PB

GRINDER
Nuova Simonelli
Mythos One

OPENING HOURS
Mon-Wed, Fri
9.30am-**5**pm
Thu **9.30**am-**4**pm

 Gluten FREE

 BEANS AVAILABLE INSTORE

 WIFI

 CYCLE FRIENDLY

 OUTDOOR seating

 DISABLED & ACCESS

 BRING YOUR OWN Cup

www.theglasshouse.cafe   T: 07800 736337
f @theglasshouseatculmvalley   @ @theglasshouse.cafe

№106 EXPLODING BAKERY

1b Central Crescent, Queen Street, Exeter, Devon, EX4 3SB

While a number of speciality ventures in Exeter have briefly blossomed before withering away, Exploding Bakery has remained a vibrant venue for fine coffee and food for almost a decade.

The perma-busy cafe is testament to the notion of doing something simple and doing it well. Founders Oli and Tom started out with the modest ambition of crafting quality caffeine and tasty traybakes from a tiny bakery next to Central Station. Nine years later the daily to-do list is much the same, just on a larger scale.

TIP A RANGE OF NATURAL WINES IS AVAILABLE AT BOTTLE SHOP PRICES

The range of signature traybakes has been fattened up to include the likes of ginger dick, almond brownie and lumberjack, all rustled up at the bakery HQ across town (which also supplies other indie cafes locally and across the UK). The coffee offering has matured too, with an inventory of roasters accompanying the house beans from Round Hill.

If you're hungry for more than coffee and cake, the open-plan kitchen also prepares a small menu of toasties, soups and salads.

ESTABLISHED
2011

KEY ROASTER
Round Hill Roastery

BREWING METHOD
Espresso, batch brew, V60

MACHINE
La Marzocco Linea

GRINDER
Mythos One x 2, Mahlkonig EK43

OPENING HOURS
Mon-Fri 8am-4pm
Sat 9am-4pm

www.explodingbakery.com   T: 01392 829787
f @explodingbakery   @explodingbakery   @explodingbakery

MAP №.107 SACRED GROUNDS

McCoy's Arcade, Fore Street, Exeter, Devon, EX4 3AN

McCoy's Arcade has long been a mecca for Exeter's creative contingent but its numbers have recently swelled thanks to the plant based foodies and caffeine conscious folk making a beeline for Sacred Grounds.

The coffee shop's founders, Hayley and Nathan Maker and Becca Allen, have championed contemporary design and fellow indies for years at their lifestyle store No Guts No Glory and this new project promotes the same causes – just via the medium of food and drink.

TIP SYRUPS ARE HOMEMADE AND THE BARISTAS HAVE NAILED OATLY LATTE ART

Even the coffee is local and indie, coming from Tiverton's Roastworks Coffee. Guests include beans roasted by Crankhouse (situated a few doors down the road).

Find the original NGNG aesthetic in the new cafe: houseplants tumble across exposed brick walls, pendant bulbs illuminate wooden tables, and a glass ceiling floods the "courtyard" with natural light.

The food is as polished as the decor and 100 per cent vegan. Feast on waffles, smorbrod and toast (toppings are updated every six weeks) followed by a slice of raw cashew-cream cheesecake.

ESTABLISHED
2018

KEY ROASTER
Roastworks
Coffee Co

BREWING METHOD
Espresso, filter

MACHINE
Fiorenzato
Ducale

GRINDER
Compak E5

OPENING HOURS
Mon-Sat **9**am-**5.30**pm
Sun **10**am-**4**pm

 Gluten FREE

 WIFI

 OUTDOOR seating

 DISABLED & ACCESS

 BRING YOUR OWN cup

 DOG FRIENDLY

www.sacredgrounds.co   T: 01392 791440

f @exetersacredgrounds   @ @exetersacredgrounds

№108 CRANKHOUSE @ 130 BASEMENT

Basement, 130 Fore Street, Exeter, Devon, EX4 3JQ

The sensory coffee experience is cranked up a notch when you're wrapped in the aroma of freshly roasted beans with the rhythmic whirr of a roasting drum playing out in the background.

It was the opportunity to create such caffeine encounters that led Dave Stanton to move his Crankhouse HQ from its Dartmoor home to a new spot in Exeter where he could assemble a team and launch a roastery-cafe. Enlisting the help of pro barista Tony and baking whizz Rosie, he's created something unique within the Devon capital.

TIP ATTENTION, BARISTAS: LOOK OUT FOR COFFEE COMPS COMING SOON

The below-pavement coffee factory has been kitted out with a handcrafted countertop where inquisitive customers can sample the latest coffees and learn about the journey of the beans from farm to filter. Regular cuppings and tastings also keep the space open after hours for those eager to glean more.

Whether you want to gen-up or chill out, the uber cool hangout – with its 70s speaker system and menagerie of droolworthy cakes – is a great spot in which to kick back in the city.

ESTABLISHED
2020

KEY ROASTER
Crankhouse Coffee

BREWING METHOD
Espresso, pourover, batch brew

MACHINE
La Marzocco Linea PB

GRINDER
Mythos One x 2, Mahlkonig EK43

OPENING HOURS
Mon-Fri 8am-4pm
Sat 9am-4pm

---

www.crankhousecoffee.co.uk   T: 07828 076596

🐦 @crankhouseroast   📷 @crankhouse130b

MAP№ 109 THE OTHER CUP

16 Market Walk, Newton Abbot, Devon, TQ12 2RX

Speciality-savvy tourists who stumble upon this Newton Abbot hangout often leave sporting a smug grin of gratification, because finding a stellar cup of single origin coffee in this slice of south Devon isn't easy.

Despite being a newbie to the speciality scene, the urban-chic coffee house has already built a firm fanbase thanks to its impressive range of high-grade beans. Respected roasteries such as Origin, Crankhouse and Round Hill supply the goods which the talented baristas fashion into meticulously prepared pourovers, batch brews and velvety-smooth espresso drinks.

INSIDER'S TIP VISIT THE WEBSITE TO FIND OUT WHICH BEANS ARE GUESTING THIS WEEK

While coffee is the main attraction, the food also deserves an honourable mention. Produce is sourced from nearby indies: fat slabs of traybake are rustled up at Exploding Bakery's Exeter HQ while sourdough is crafted at The Almond Thief Bakery in Dartington.

We recommend visiting for a lazy afternoon indulging in a chunky grilled cheese sandwich followed by a wedge of lemon, polenta and pistachio cake paired with a bright 'n' beautiful batch brew

ESTABLISHED
2019

KEY ROASTER
Multiple roasters

BREWING METHOD
Espresso, V60, AeroPress, Clever Dripper, batch brew

MACHINE
Sanremo Opera

GRINDER
Victoria Arduino Mythos, Mahlkonig EK43

OPENING HOURS
Mon-Fri 8am-4.30pm
Sat 9am-5pm
Sun 10am-4pm

---

www.theothercup.co.uk   T: 07585 771986

f @theothercup   @ @theothercup

MAP 110 KALIPSO ARTISAN COFFEE & FOOD

45 Fleet Street, Torquay, Devon, TQ2 5DW

The overwhelming prospect of choosing between numerous good coffee venues in a big city isn't a problem for Torquay's visitors as Kalipso is the only indie crafting speciality on the high street.

Tourists visiting the English Riviera, as well as locals who've become loyal to the cafe after tasting the Colonna house beans, throng here for a quality caffeine fix. In summer you'll find them clustered around the cotton-wheel tables out front, while in the colder months patrons head indoors to lounge on the brown leather banquettes.

Despite the seaside town's general dearth of speciality haunts, Kalipso more than fills the gap thanks to its bumper selection of beans and specialist drinks list. Guest coffees are sourced from big names such as Square Mile, Clifton, Origin, Hasbean and Crankhouse and can be prepared in a multitude of serve styles. Niche specials include pistachio latte, coconut cream coffee and chocolate orange mocha.

INSIDER'S TIP COOL DOWN IN SUMMER WITH A GLASS OF HOMEMADE LEMONADE

The food offering is headlined by New York-style bagels: pastrami, red leicester and gherkin is the current number one crowd-pleaser.

ESTABLISHED
2015

KEY ROASTER
Colonna Coffee

BREWING METHOD
Espresso, V60, AeroPress, Chemex, cold brew

MACHINE
La Marzocco Linea

GRINDER
Mahlkonig K30 Vario, Mahlkonig Tanzania, Mazzer Mini

OPENING HOURS
Mon-Sat 8.30am-6pm
Sun 9am-6pm

T: 01803 213728
f @kalipsocoffee @kalipsocoffee

MAP№ 111 THE HAIRY BARISTA

69 High Street, Totnes, Devon, TQ9 5PB

Sustainable-savvy Totnes isn't short of vegan dining options but, if you're craving quality speciality coffee to go with your plant-based brekkie, head to this lively cafe at the top of the High Street.

London's Mission Coffee Works provides the house roast which owner Roee Yekutiel crafts into syrupy espresso on his gleaming Sanremo Opera 2. Filter options are fortified with guests from speciality stalwarts such as Square Mile, Hasbean and Crankhouse.

☞TIP STOCK UP ON COFFEE, CHAI, HOT CHOC AND BREW GEAR

If you're already at peak caffeine capacity let Roee whip you up one of his mean organic matcha lattes, an unusual mushroom hot chocolate or, for those on a wellness kick, an organic superfood smoothie.

Veg-centric finds here include healthy breakfasts, seasonal soups and sourdough toasties, while vegan and gluten-free locally baked cakes tempt the sweet toothed of all dining persuasions.

Roee and wife Ruth Harris are committed to reducing their impact on the environment via the use of compostable packaging, reusable cups, stainless steel straws and fresh Totnes-made almond milk (which comes in glass bottles).

ESTABLISHED
2017

KEY ROASTER
Mission Coffee Works

BREWING METHOD
Espresso, cafetiere

MACHINE
Sanremo Opera 2

GRINDER
Mythos One, Mahlkonig EK43

OPENING HOURS
Mon-Fri 8am-5pm
Sat 9am-5pm

T: 01803 867773
f @thehairybarista @the.hairy.barista

ROASTERIES

№114
Voyager Coffee

MAP: 112 ROASTWORKS COFFEE CO.

Unit 7, Blackdown Park, Willand, Devon, EX15 2FS

Looking for love of the caffeinated kind? Search no further than Roastworks' Singles Club which was launched last year to pair coffee lovers with the bean of their dreams. It's all part of the roastery's ongoing effort to get the public falling for speciality.

The Club sees founder Will Little and his roasting matchmakers cup hundreds of coffees in order to curate a collection of very special beans from the top tier of global coffees. Their aim? *'To find the most incredible, bonkers and delicious coffees,'* says Will.

Bean geeks can swipe right on the current coffee on the roaster's website. Previous flings have included the apple pie-esque Cordillera Del Fuego from Costa Rica (an anaerobically fermented natural) and the melon-liqueur-flavoured Sumatran natural Asman Arianto.

'BEAN GEEKS CAN SWIPE RIGHT ON THE CURRENT COFFEE'

The matchmaking doesn't stop there either as the team are pressing on with supporting their wholesale customers by supplying grinders and machines via a new partnership with Victoria Arduino.

ESTABLISHED
2014

ROASTER
MAKE & SIZE
G.W. Barth
Menado 60kg
Probat LG 12kg

OPEN
BY APPOINTMENT

BEANS AVAILABLE
ONLINE ONSITE

---

www.roastworks.co.uk T: 01884 829400

f @roastworkscoffeeco @roastworks_coffee_co

MAP 113 CRANKHOUSE COFFEE

Basement, 130 Fore Street, Exeter, Devon, EX4 3JQ

Devon's Crankhouse Coffee has enjoyed a pinnacle year in its development. Starting the decade with a bang, founder Dave Stanton moved Crankhouse HQ from its edge-of-Dartmoor home to a swish new set-up a stone's throw from the centre of Exeter. The move made room for a new on-site cafe where customers can sample the latest espresso blends and single origins.

In the run up to the relocation, Dave also doubled his one-man operation to a roasting team of two by welcoming English AeroPress Champ Lewis Tanner to the fold. Crankhouse also managed to squeeze in a stellar performance at the UK Roasting Championships (and a spot in the top five.)

'CRANKHOUSE CLOCKED UP A RECORD 1,937 ROASTS'

The roastery has come a long way since its humble beginnings in Dave's garage and, in 2019, it clocked up a record 1,937 roasts – including four blends and 67 single origins from 71 different coffees.

ESTABLISHED
2014

ROASTER
MAKE & SIZE
Petroncini TT7.5

IKAWA sample roaster

CAFE ONSITE

OPEN BY APPOINTMENT

COFFEE COURSES

BEANS AVAILABLE
ONLINE ONSITE

---

www.crankhousecoffee.co.uk   T: 07588 020288

f @crankhousecoffee   🐦 @crankhouseroast   📷 @crankhouseroast

MAP №114 VOYAGER COFFEE

The Roastery, Mardle Way Business Park, Buckfastleigh, Devon, TQ11 0JL

Living and working on the edge of rugged Dartmoor hasn't only inspired the team at Voyager to roast coffee in tune with the unique terroir; the stunning landscape has also ignited a passionate eco perspective.

The gang are on a mission to implement planet-positive change without compromising on quality. And they're doing a darn good job of it: a circular packaging system bundles beans into bags (made from plants, using less energy and emitting less CO_2 during production than traditional packaging) which can be fully composted.

'ON A MISSION TO IMPLEMENT PLANET-POSITIVE CHANGE'

The same focus on quality is adopted when it comes to bronzing the beans, something the haul of gongs from the Great Taste Awards 2019 attests to. Going down a storm is the black honey processed coffee from Los Pirineos in El Salvador, which wows via almost any brew method with its juicy, super-sweet and full-bodied flavour.

ESTABLISHED
2000

ROASTER
MAKE & SIZE
Genio 30kg
Genio 15kg

OPEN BY APPOINTMENT

COFFEE COURSES

COURSES

BEANS AVAILABLE ONLINE

www.voyagercoffee.co.uk   T: 01364 644440

f @voyagercoffeeroasters   @ @voyagercoffee

MAP Nº 115 THE DEVON COFFEE COMPANY

195 Faraday Mill Business Park, Plymouth, Devon, PL4 0ST

Any cafe buying coffee from this award winning Plymouth roastery automatically gets to enjoy the perks of technical support and access to its new state-of-the-art barista training campus.

'We run workshops and SCA courses three days a week, allowing our trade customers to acquire the skills to deliver a consistent, high-quality coffee offering,' says head roaster Andrew Baker.

'We're also opening our doors to the public for monthly after-hours tasting sessions and workshops, helping home enthusiasts experience what it's like to be a barista – or simply to sample diverse speciality coffee from around the world.'

ESTABLISHED
2011

ROASTER
MAKE & SIZE
Besca 15kg
North 1kg

OPEN
BY APPOINTMENT

COFFEE
COURSES

COURSES

BEANS
AVAILABLE
ONLINE ONSITE

"WE'RE OPENING OUR DOORS FOR MONTHLY AFTER-HOURS TASTING SESSIONS AND WORKSHOPS"

For a second season in a row the gang have sourced coffee from the emerging market of Myanmar, as well as from well-established coffee origins such as Ethiopia, Colombia and Brazil.

'We're also excited to be working with the all-female growers of La Yerba in Mexico,' adds Andrew.

www.devoncoffeecompany.com   T: 01752 222567

f @devoncoffeecompany   🐦 @devoncoffeeco   📷 @devoncoffeecompany

SHORT & STRONG
HOT DRINKS

ESPRESSO
MACCHIATO
AMERICANO
PICCOLO
FLAT WHITE
CAPPUCINO
LATTE
MATCHA LATTE
ICED COFFEE

HOT CHOCOLATE
HOT CHOC - THE WORKS
GOLDEN TUMERIC MILK

TEA

BREAKFAST TEA
DECAF TEA

TREGOTHNAN TEA
CLASSIC TEA
PEPPERMINT
RED BERRY
MANUKA
EARL GREY
CHAM
GR

CORNWALL

Nº120
Short & Strong

CAFES

ROASTERIES

*All locations are approximate

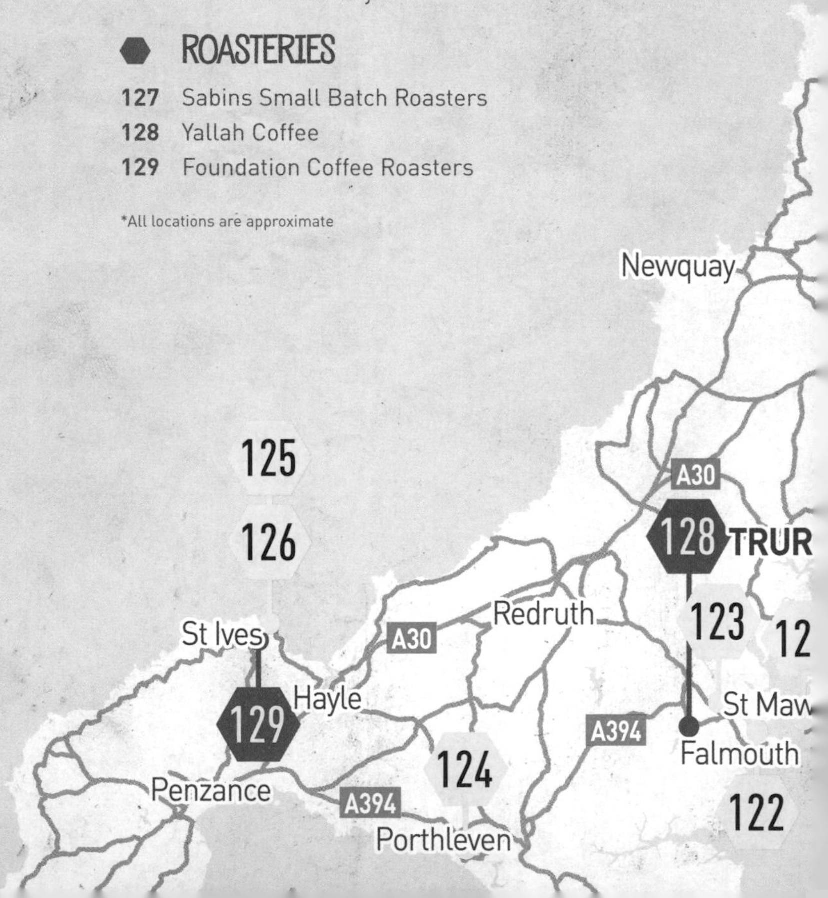

Newquay

125

126

A30

128 TRUR

Redruth

St Ives   A30

123   **12**

Hayle

129

A394   St Maw

Penzance   A394   Falmouth

124

Porthleven   **122**

№116 LIBERTY COFFEE

4 Northgate Street, Launceston, Cornwall, PL15 8BD

This cafe on the Devon-Cornwall border has been an institution for speciality-savvy sippers since 2013, with tourists travelling between the counties often rerouting via Launceston for their just-off-the-A30 fix.

Liberty continues to uphold its six-year rep for consistently great caffeine thanks to founder Ben Statton's regular rejuvenations. This year he's added a kitchen to the premises to expand the menu of savoury eats and bolster the already popular range of homemade bakes. Customers are now revelling in fresh-from-the-oven frittata slices, gourmet sausage rolls and bowls of steaming soup served with Coombeshead Farm sourdough.

TIP PARK YOURSELF ON THE SOFA AND PAIR YOUR SIP WITH SOME CAFFEINATED READING MATERIAL

The coffee menu appeals to all manner of passersby, and crowd-pleasers such as the Hasbean house espresso are served alongside more exotic beans from a roll call of guest roasters. Ben changes the line-up regularly and you'll usually find beans from a couple of South West roasteries on the bill – sample them as drip filter.

ESTABLISHED
2013

KEY ROASTER
Hasbean Coffee

BREWING METHOD
Espresso,
Kalita Wave

MACHINE
La Marzocco
Linea

GRINDER
Mythos One

OPENING HOURS
Mon-Sat 9am-5pm

---

www.liberty-coffee.co.uk   T: 01566 776751

f @libcoffee   @libcoffee   @libcoffee

MAP№ 117 ST KEW FARMSHOP & CAFE

St Kew Highway, Bodmin, Cornwall, PL30 3EF

The term 'hidden gem' is somewhat overused in food and travel writing, but this beautiful farm shop and cafe on the Atlantic Highway is the real deal.

Sleepy north Cornwall may not be the obvious place to look for hip Scandi-style interiors, wood fired feasting or stonking speciality coffee, but here it is.

☰TIP ATTEND AN EVENING DINING EVENT TO FEAST ON FOOD COOKED IN THE WOOD-FIRED BREAD OVEN

Josh and Sarah have been quietly beavering away since they took over in 2017, introducing a luscious array of houseplants and local produce to the retail section as well as working with Cornish beansmiths Yallah to take the coffee next level. They're currently serving the roastery's Trust blend as espresso-based drinks, though plans are afoot to introduce additional serve styles in the near future.

Complement your fine brew with hearty rustic food which is all made in-house – including the cakes and puds. Delicious soups, hearty sandwiches, vegan salad bowls and seasonal specials such as the Mediterranean bruschetta keep things fresh and interesting.

ESTABLISHED
2017

KEY ROASTER
Yallah Coffee

BREWING METHOD
Espresso

MACHINE
Victoria Arduino White Eagle

GRINDER
Victoria Arduino Mythos One

OPENING HOURS
Mon-Sat 9am-5pm
Sun 9.30am-4pm

Gluten FREE · BEANS AVAILABLE INSTORE · WIFI · CYCLE FRIENDLY · OUTDOOR SEATING · DISABLED ACCESS · BRING YOUR OWN CUP · DOG FRIENDLY

www.stkewfarmshop.co.uk
f @St Kew Farm Shop & Cafe @stkewfarmshop

№ 118 FEE'S FOOD

Pavilion Stores, Rock Road, Rock, Cornwall, PL27 6JT

If every village had a Fee's Food to keep its residents so expertly fed and watered, no one would ever choose to live in the city.

For this tiny shop on Rock's small parade of upmarket stores is a stuffed pantry of homemade lasagna and crumbles which also features a groaning deli, shelf of locally baked sourdough and a brew bar serving cracking speciality coffee.

Yallah supplies the beans – care of its Trust range – which Fee's son George and the team turn into well-crafted espresso drinks, delivered in pottery cups created up the road by a lady named Debbie.

TIP THE SMOKED HADDOCK RAREBIT, CRAB APPLE JELLY AND CORNISH FISH PIE ARE FEE'S FANS' FAVES

Fee does the cooking in her nearby pro kitchen, supplying the store and myriad external clients (via the catering arm of the business) with smart homecooked food. For Wednesday-night-supper ease, many of the dishes are frozen and ready to be popped in the oven (pass them off as your own).

Swing by for a short black, empty your wallet on too-appealing-to-leave-behind goodies and revel in your good fortune to do all this with a side order of sea air.

ESTABLISHED
2018

KEY ROASTER
Yallah Coffee

BREWING METHOD
Espresso, filter

MACHINE
Victoria Arduino
White Eagle

GRINDER
Mythos One

OPENING HOURS
Mon-Sat **8**am-**6**pm
Sun **10**am-**2**pm
(reduced in winter)

---

www.feesfood.co.uk   T: 01208 869222

@fees_food

MAP№ 119 STRONG ADOLFOS

Hawksfield, A39, St Breock, Wadebridge, Cornwall, PL27 7LR

Seasoned beach-seekers and wave-riders travelling along Cornwall's north coast schedule an extra hour into their journey for an expertly caffeinated break at this unlikely find on the A39.

Strong Adolfos' mission to redefine the roadside pit stop has been a game-changer since 2013, and the perma-busy indie continues to refuel weary drivers (and their passengers) with quality caffeine and homemade fodder. Cornwall-roasted batch brew and flawless flat whites are the new service station standard around here.

TIP DECKING PROVIDES ALFRESCO SIPPING SPACE IN SUMMER

A line-up of globally inspired (with Scandi emphasis) breakfast and lunch dishes means it's worth pulling your KeepCup away and sitting in. Take some time out to tuck in to house specials like nasi goreng, Yarg fritter salad and Indian-spiced monkfish skewers, followed by a sizeable slice of cake from the incredible collection.

Full-tummied and revitalised, stretch your muscles before the next leg of your trip by taking a wander around Hawksfield's deli, apparel store and classic car and motorcycle showroom downstairs.

ESTABLISHED
2013

KEY ROASTER
Origin Coffee Roasters

BREWING METHOD
Espresso, batch filter

MACHINE
La Marzocco Linea PB Auto Brew Ratio

GRINDER
Nuova Simonelli Mythos One

OPENING HOURS
Mon-Fri 8.30am-4pm
Sat-Sun 9am-4pm

Gluten FREE

BEANS AVAILABLE
INSTORE

WIFI

CYCLE FRIENDLY

OUTDOOR seating

DISABLED ACCESS

BRING YOUR OWN Cup

DOG FRIENDLY

---

www.strongadolfos.com T: 01208 816949

f @strongadolfos 🐦 @strongadolfos 📷 @strongadolfos

№120 SHORT & STRONG

Charlestown Road, Charlestown, Cornwall, PL25 3NJ

Short & Strong was founded on its owners John, Mel and Tom's shared passion for quality coffee (served short and strong, naturally).

The trio got the coffee bug while travelling in Oz and decided to haul a slice of antipodean coffee culture back to the historic harbour village of Charlestown.

They set up shop in a former mast shed which they turned into a cosy cafe – a symphony of rough-hewn wood, plants and quirky artwork. Indeed, there's a certain irony to the fact that the village's glorious original tall ships and ye olde worlde charm, which have long drawn swathes of day-tripping crowds, now compete for visitors' attention with a contemporary cafe serving Origin Coffee and modern brekkies and lunches.

TIP SATURDAY BRUNCH? UPSTAIRS SISTER VENUE THE LONGSTORE FEATURES EXTENDED MENUS

Of course, bean geeks would pick head barista Ross' expertly pulled espresso, batch or cold brew over an impressive hull every time – especially when paired with a homemade Cornish sausage roll or one of the Da Bara bakery delights in the cake cabinet.

ESTABLISHED
2016

KEY ROASTER
Origin Coffee Roasters

BREWING METHOD
Espresso, V60, filter, cold brew, batch brew, Kalita Wave

MACHINE
La Marzocco Linea PB

GRINDER
Victoria Arduino Mythos One, Mahlkonig EK43

OPENING HOURS
Sun-Fri 9am-4pm
Sat 8am-4pm

Gluten FREE

BEANS AVAILABLE INSTORE

WIFI

CYCLE FRIENDLY

OUTDOOR SEATING

DISABLED ACCESS

BRING YOUR OWN CUP

DOG FRIENDLY

---

www.shortandstrong.co.uk
f @shortandstrongcafe @shortandstrongctown

MAP 121 BEAR CORNWALL

St Mawes Castle Car Park, Castle Drive, St Mawes, Cornwall, TR2 5DE

Two very distinct pieces of history sit side by side on the stunning Cornish headland at St Mawes. One is Henry VIII's 16th century St Mawes Castle; the other is Nigel Cullen's immaculately restored 1969 Citroen HY van.

Nigel set up Bear Cornwall (named after his son Harris Bear, FYI) in the English Heritage car park at the end of August 2019 and has already won a legion of fans who are prepared to go out of their way for his fine speciality coffee.

INSIDER TIP: OPENING HOURS ARE EXTENDED FOR FAL RIVER WEEK, FALMOUTH AIR SHOW AND OTHER LOCAL EVENTS

The beans (appropriately named Knockout) are roasted just across the water in Penryn by Olfactory and are the lovechild of lots from Costa Rica, Mexico and Brazil. Expect juicy and sweet red grape and cacao nib notes and, if you really want to draw out the fudgy flavours, add luscious Cornish whole milk from The Free Range Dairy.

Bear Cornwall is open from Easter to late October and on weekends in winter, so put this one on your hit list for a visit and the opportunity to delight in the perfect pairing of a beautifully crafted coffee with a crisp and buttery Da Bara Bakery cinnamon bun.

ESTABLISHED
2019

KEY ROASTER
Olfactory Coffee Roasters

BREWING METHOD
Espresso

MACHINE
La Marzocco Linea 2 AV

GRINDER
Mythos One

OPENING HOURS
Mon-Sun 10am-4pm
(weekends-only in winter)

 Gluten FREE

 BEANS AVAILABLE INSTORE

 CYCLE FRIENDLY

 OUTDOOR SEATING

 DISABLED ACCESS

 BRING YOUR OWN CUP

 DOG FRIENDLY

T: 07980 933839
 f @bearcornwallcoffee @bear_cornwall

№122 GYLLY BEACH CAFE

Gyllyngvase Beach, Cliff Road, Falmouth, Cornwall, TR11 4PA

Cornwall's beaches helped England secure the number two spot on *Lonely Planet*'s Best in Travel 2020 Top Countries list and there are few more charming examples than Gyllyngvase. Fortunately for visitors to Falmouth it's also home to one of the country's best-positioned speciality coffee spots.

Fine white sands and gentle waves make a breathtaking backdrop for a mid-morning coffee; cradle a Cornwall-roasted Origin flat white while you watch the paddleboarders from the picture windows.

In high summer the place buzzes with foodies and coffee fiends taking advantage of the all-day menu, but don't be deterred if it's packed out as the team thrive on a full house (and have even installed a four-group-head espresso machine to meet demand).

ESTABLISHED
2002

KEY ROASTER
Origin Coffee Roasters

BREWING METHOD
Espresso

MACHINE
La Marzocco

GRINDER
Nuova Simonelli Mythos One

OPENING HOURS
Mon-Sun 9am-late

📍TIP RETURN AFTER DARK FOR A DECADENT EVENING DINING EXPERIENCE

Food is as much of a draw as the coffee and head chef Dale McIntosh excels in classic casual-dining dishes which he kicks up a notch come evening. Creations like crab ravioli with velvet swimmer crab bisque, beach vegetables, sea spinach oil and oyster leaf warrant a return trip later in the day.

---

www.gyllybeach.com   T: 01326 312884

f @gyllybeachcafe   🐦 @gyllybeachcafe   📷 @gyllybeachcafe

MAP№ 123 ORIGIN COFFEE ROASTERS – THE WAREHOUSE

Commercial Road, Penryn, Cornwall, TR10 8AE

Having recently celebrated its 15th anniversary – and been voted the UK's top speciality roaster at the Allegra Europe & Middle East Coffee Awards – Origin enjoys renowned status in the speciality coffee world.

Head to its Penryn outpost for a slice of Hoxton-by-harbour, thanks to the sleek interior decor, delicious brews and curated brunch menus which celebrate the best local and seasonal produce.

INSIDERS TIP LOOK OUT FOR NEW COFFEE LOTS FROM PERU AND TANZANIA

Sipping a stellar single origin brew alongside your food is obligatory. Choose from classic espresso options, plus pourover and batch filter. Whichever gets your vote, you're assured of a fresh and fragrant roast, expertly prepped by a skilled team.

Origin's thirst for new flavours is as keen as ever and its direct-trade relationships continue to grow organically. Beans travel to the Helston roastery from Ethiopia, Brazil and Panama among other locations across the world. The team love to explore experimental lots and roast to showcase the exceptional flavours.

ESTABLISHED
2018

KEY ROASTER
Origin Coffee Roasters

BREWING METHOD
Espresso, batch filter, pourover

MACHINE
La Marzocco KB90

GRINDER
Victoria Arduino Mythos One

OPENING HOURS
Mon-Sat **8**am-**5**pm
Sun **9**am-**4**pm

 Gluten FREE

 BEANS AVAILABLE INSTORE

 WIFI

 CYCLE FRIENDLY

 OUTDOOR SEATING

 DISABLED ACCESS

BRING YOUR OWN Cup

 DOG FRIENDLY

www.origincoffee.co.uk   T: 01326 617100

f @origincoffeeroasters   🐦 @origincoffee   📷 @origincoffeeshops

SKIP THE
LACTOSE
NOT THE LATTE

Help your customers feel good* by skipping the lactose, not the latte, with Arla LactoFREE.

Demand is rising for great tasting dairy that's easier to digest,** so stock up now.

Arla
Lacto
FREE

SEMI SKIMMED
MILK DRINK

ALL NATURAL INGREDIENTS · PACKED WITH NUTRIENTS* · EASIER TO DIGEST**

FREE FROM LACTOSE

FIND OUT MORE AT ARLAPRO.CO.UK

*Vit B12 contributes to the reduction of tiredness and fatigue. Calcium is needed for the maintenance of normal bones. Protein contributes to growth in muscle mass.

**Easier to digest for those who may have gastro-intestinal discomfort caused by lactose intake.

Arla®

MAP№ 124 ORIGIN COFFEE ROASTERS – HARBOUR HEAD

Harbour Head, Porthleven, Cornwall, TR13 9JY

Breezy Porthleven is where the Origin story began and, 15 years on, it's still the perfect place to appreciate the iconic roastery's fine coffee.

Poured concrete and industrial fittings lend a contemporary edge to reclaimed timber and vintage furniture, and the relaxed spot has been recognised for both its outstanding coffee and views to match.

The Origin coffee programme is based on crop seasonality and draws from producers across the world to deliver a consistently delicious cup. Responsible sourcing is woven into the roastery's DNA with direct-trade producer relationships ensuring the beans delivered to the Helston roastery are fairly sourced and of the highest quality.

TIP QUIRKY ILLUSTRATIONS FROM EIGHT ARTISTS FEATURE ON ORIGIN'S 15TH ANNIVERSARY PACKAGING

Harbour Head's highly trained baristas do justice to the beans via a La Marzocco Strada (for espresso options) while batch brew and pourover preps are available too. Take the experience next-level with the sugary-lipped thrill of a Da Bara Bakery cinnamon bun.

ESTABLISHED
2013

KEY ROASTER
Origin Coffee
Roasters

BREWING METHOD
Espresso,
batch filter,
pourover

MACHINE
La Marzocco
Strada

GRINDER
Victoria Arduino
Mythos One x 2,
Mahlkonig EK43

OPENING HOURS
Mon-Sun **9**am-**5**pm
(March-October)

 Gluten FREE

 BEANS AVAILABLE INSTORE

 WIFI

 CYCLE FRIENDLY

 OUTDOOR SEATING

 BRING YOUR OWN Cup.

 DOG FRIENDLY

---

www.origincoffee.co.uk   T: 01326 574337

f @origincoffeeroasters   **𝕏** @origincoffee   **◎** @origincoffeeshops

MAP No. 125 YALLAH COFFEE KIOSK

Court Arcade, Wharf Road, St Ives, Cornwall, TR26 1LF

A view from the brew bar isn't necessarily a priority for espresso slingers but, for the baristas at Yallah's St Ives hub, steaming milk while gazing over a wide expanse of turquoise blue harbour is a perk of the job.

Tucked away behind two bright green shutters on the busy waterfront, this hole-in-the-wall espresso bar is a sanity-saver for caffeine-hungry beachgoers, gallery hoppers and walkers who stray off the South West Coast Path. A reverse-mermaid (bikini body, fish head) mural further signals where to find the good stuff.

INSIDER'S TIP DOUGHNUTS AND OONA'S CAKES OFFER DROOLWORTHY ACCOMPANIMENTS TO THE CAFFEINE

The Kiosk may be dinky but its takeaway offering certainly isn't. Own-roasted beans are served as espresso and batch brew, while cold brew makes an appearance in warmer months. And, thanks to a carousel of beans, there's always something new to savour, including fruit-forward and opinion-splitting coffees (this is where the roastery tries out new and unusual finds). Those at peak caffeine will find cold-pressed juices as alternative refreshment.

Any coffee spot that lists 'plastic-free' as one of its creds deserves a shoutout, and worthy of a mention are the reusable milk tubs and custom-fitted Milkit dispenser.

ESTABLISHED
2018

KEY ROASTER
Yallah Coffee

BREWING METHOD
Espresso,
batch brew,
cold brew

MACHINE
Sanremo
Café Racer

GRINDER
Mahlkonig EK43,
Compak

OPENING HOURS
Mon-Sun 8am-4pm

www.yallahcoffee.co.uk   T: 01326 727383

f @yallahcoffee   @ @yallahkiosk

^{MAP №}126 THE YELLOW CANARY

12 Fore Street, St Ives, Cornwall, TR26 1AB

For nearly 50 years, The Yellow Canary has fuelled St Ives' holidaymakers and locals with fine coffee and scrumptious food from its vibrant space on cobbled Fore Street.

Its name – a reference to the now-antiquated use of canaries in mining to detect deadly gases (if the bird fell from its perch, the miner would know it was time to leave) – is also a clue as to how long this Cornish institution has been in operation.

^{INSIDER'S} TIP DOORSTEP SOURDOUGH SARNIES AND HOMEMADE BAKES ARE PERFECT COFFEE-PAIRING MATERIAL

To keep the cafe in tune with modern times, the Haase family (who've been in charge for half a century) recently rolled out a Scandi-inspired refurb. Thanks to its newly polished floor, pared-back scattering of seats and freshly painted walls, this Yellow Canary is gleaming.

The coffee offering is also about to have an overhaul and the seriously good house beans roasted by Origin in Cornwall will be joined by guests from the likes of Round Hill, new extraction equipment, an expanded range of brewing methods and more retail coffee kit.

ESTABLISHED
1972

KEY ROASTER
Origin Coffee Roasters

BREWING METHOD
Espresso, filter, batch brew

MACHINE
La Marzocco Linea

GRINDER
Mythos One, Mahlkonig EK43, Mazzer Major E

OPENING HOURS
Mon-Sun **9**am-**5**pm
(extended in summer)

T: 01736 797118

 @theyellowcanarycafe   @theyellowcanarycafe

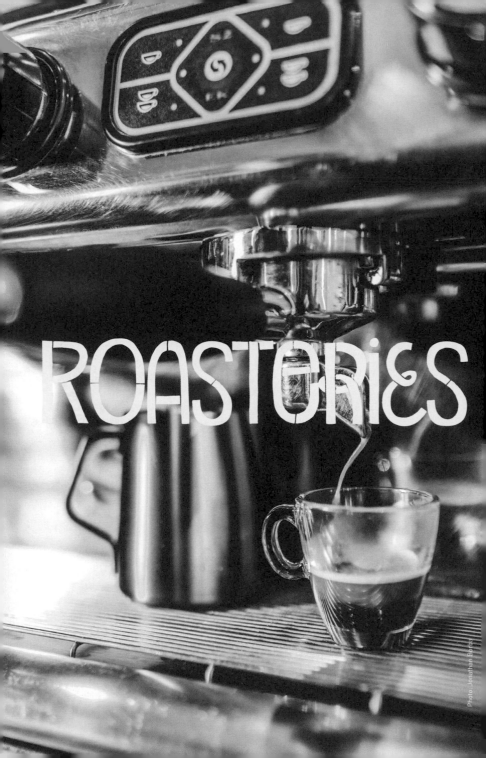

ROASTORIES

MAP 127 SABINS SMALL BATCH ROASTERS

Butterfly Barn, Hersham, Bude, Cornwall, EX23 9LZ

The Sabins gang have long been coffee trailblazers, although in a quiet sort of way. Since 2014, Paul and Emma have run their roastery out of a small shack while simultaneously home schooling six children and keeping horses. During this time they've also supported the education of two young chaps on the other side of the world through their Community Espresso SOS Africa coffee.

This year will see another change as, thanks to the steady organic growth of the business, they are about to (sustainably) self build a new, larger roastery. Paul and Emma are also developing relationships with two coffee farmers in the hope of establishing their first continuous direct trade and will soon take their inaugural origin trip to one of the co-operatives they buy from.

'COFFEE GROUNDS ARE USED TO MAKE ECO FIRELIGHTERS'

Planet-pleasing practices have long been a priority: all beans are sold in refillable tins or home-compostable, plant-based bags, while wholesale customers receive theirs in food-grade containers. Used grounds are then collected by Sabins to make eco firelighters.

ESTABLISHED
2014

ROASTER
MAKE & SIZE
Toper 1kg x 2

OPEN
BY APPOINTMENT

COFFEE
COURSES

BEANS
AVAILABLE

---

www.sabinscoffee.co.uk   T: 01288 321159

f @sabinscoffee   🐦 @sabinscoffee   📷 @sabins_coffee

MAP№128 YALLAH COFFEE

The Roastery, Argal Home Farm, Kergilliack, Falmouth, Cornwall, TR11 5PD

Roasting coffee in the wilds of Cornwall makes it pretty easy to be aware of the natural environment and the need to protect it, which may be one of the reasons why the Yallah crew are so committed to running their business in a planet-friendly fashion.

The pioneering speciality roastery not only generates its own solar electricity (there are 94 panels on the roof) and hot water from an on-site biomass boiler, it's also about to convert its roaster from gas (which forms a significant chunk of its carbon output) to electricity – probably the first roastery in the South West to do this.

ESTABLISHED
2014

ROASTER
MAKE & SIZE
Virey Gamier
15kg
Otto Swadlo 3kg

OPEN
BY APPOINTMENT

COFFEE
COURSES

BEANS
AVAILABLE
ONLINE | ONSITE

'RUNNING THEIR BUSINESS IN A PLANET-FRIENDLY FASHION'

In addition, Yallah offsets its carbon emissions (including those that result from the shipping of the green beans to the roastery) by planting trees in Scotland.

Don't be fooled into thinking the focus here is purely on the environment as the sourcing of exceptional beans is what really gets the team enthused. Find Yallah coffee across the county and visit the Kiosk in St Ives to experience its more unusual discoveries.

www.yallahcoffee.co.uk T: 01326 727383
f @yallahcoffee 🐦 @yallahcoffee 📷 @yallahcoffee

MAP № 129 FOUNDATION COFFEE ROASTERS

Unit 1, Penbeagle Industrial Estate, St Ives, Cornwall, TR26 2JH

Foundation's founders Jack and Marco believe in the power of small actions to make a big difference, which is why they've considered sustainability and responsibility at every stage of production at their St Ives roastery. As keen surfers, it certainly makes sense that they're committed to doing everything they can to protect the natural environment.

Foundation uses ethically and fairly traded beans from across the world's coffee growing belt, which are cooked up on a 15kg Giesen into a series of house blends and an ever-changing selection of single origins. A particular favourite is the Ethiopian Yirgacheffe Chelelektu with its notes of juicy strawberry.

'JACK AND MARCO BELIEVE IN THE POWER OF SMALL ACTIONS TO MAKE A BIG DIFFERENCE'

Coffee is delivered to the likes of Porthminster Beach Café and Blue Bar in Porthtowan in reusable 4kg buckets, while 100 per cent home-compostable bags are used for subscriptions and retail.

ESTABLISHED
2019

ROASTER
MAKE & SIZE
Giesen W15A

BEANS AVAILABLE
ONLINE / ONSITE

www.foundationroasters.co.uk   T: 07702 311595

f @foundationroasters   🐦 @foundationroas1   📷 @foundationroasters

MORE GOOD finDS

MORE GOOD
COFFEE SHOPS

MORE EXCEPTIONAL PLACES TO DRINK COFFEE ...

130
108 COFFEE HOUSE
109 Kenwyn Street, Truro,
Cornwall, TR1 3DJ

131
12 BEACH RD
12 Beach Road, Newquay,
Cornwall, TR7 1ES
www.12beachroad.co.uk

132
ALBATROSS CAFE
60 North Street, Bedminster,
Bristol, BS3 1HJ
www.albatrosscafebristol.business.site

133
ANNA CAKE COUTURE
7a Boyce's Avenue, Clifton,
Bristol, BS8 4AA
www.thisisanna.co.uk

134
BAKESMITHS
65 Whiteladies Road, Bristol, BS8 2LY
www.bakesmiths.co.uk

135
BEACON COFFEE
28a High Street, Falmouth,
Cornwall, TR11 2AD
www.beaconcoffee.co.uk

136
BIKE SHED CAFE
The Square, Barnstaple,
Devon, EX32 8LS
www.bikesheduk.com

137
BOO'S KITCHEN
2 Woodville Road, Mumbles,
Swansea, SA3 4AD

138
BOX & BARBER COFFEE HOUSE
82 Fore Street, Newquay,
Cornwall, TR7 1EY

139
BREWED
136 Lewes Road, Brighton,
East Sussex, BN2 3LG
www.brewedroasters.co.uk

140
BUN + BEAN
8 Mount Pleasant, Lewes,
East Sussex, BN7 2DH
www.bunandbean.com

141
CAMBER
Unit 3, Lawrence Hill Industrial Estate,
Russell Town Avenue, Redfield,
Bristol, BS5 9LT
www.businessasusual.cc/camber

142
CHARLIE FRIDAY'S COFFEE SHOP
Church Hill, Lynton, Devon, EX35 6HY
www.charliefridayscoffeeshop.co.uk

143
COALTOWN ESPRESSO BAR
4 The Arcade, College Street,
Ammanford, Carmarthenshire, SA18 2LN
www.coaltowncoffee.co.uk

144
COALTOWN ROASTERY CANTEEN
Coaltown Roastery, Foundry Road,
Ammanford, Carmarthenshire, SA18 2LS
www.coaltowncoffee.co.uk

145
COASTERS COFFEE COMPANY
1 Abbots Quay, Prince of Wales Road,
Kingsbridge, Devon, TQ7 1DY

146
COFFEE & VINYL
38 Tor Hill Road, Torquay, Devon, TQ2 5RF

147
COFFEE + BEER
16 Cotham Hill, Bristol, BS6 6LF
www.coffeeandbeer.co.uk

148
COFFEE@33
33 Trafalgar Street, Brighton,
East Sussex, BN1 4ED

149
CONVOY ESPRESSO
The Paintworks, Bath Road, Bristol, BS4 3EH
www.convoyespresso.com

150
DEVON COFFEE
88 Queen Street, Exeter, Devon, EX4 3RP

151
DOUGH LOVER
99 Trafalgar Street, Brighton,
East Sussex, BN1 4ER
www.doughlover.com

152
DOWN TO EARTH COFFEE
75 Western Road, Hove,
East Sussex, BN3 2JQ

153
EXE COFFEE ROASTERS
19 Heavitree Road, Exeter,
Devon, EX1 2LD
www.execoffeeroasters.co.uk

154
FED 303
303 Gloucester Road, Bristol, BS7 8PE
www.fedcafe.co.uk

155
FULL COURT PRESS
59 Broad Street, Bristol, BS1 2EJ
www.fcp.coffee

156
GLAZED
25 Ditchling Road, Brighton,
East Sussex, BN1 4SB
www.glazedcoffee.co.uk

157
GOOD VIBES CAFE
28 Killigrew Street, Falmouth,
Cornwall, TR11 3PN

158
HANGRY
68 Ebrington Street, Plymouth,
Devon, PL4 9AQ
www.hangryrestaurants.co.uk

159
HARD LINES CAFE & ROASTERY
St Cana Court, Cowbridge Road East,
Canton, Cardiff, CF5 1GX
www.hard-lines.co.uk

160
HARD LINES – CARDIFF CENTRAL MARKET
Unit 25, Cardiff Central Market,
St Mary's Street, Cardiff, CF10 1AU
www.hard-lines.co.uk

161
HATTERS COFFEE HOUSE
21 Fore Street, Redruth, Cornwall, TR15 2BD

162
HEARTBREAK HOTEL COFFEE – WOOLACOMBE
Lower Byways, The Esplanade,
Woolacombe, Devon, EX34 7DJ
www.heartbreakhotelcoffee.com

163
HOXTON BAKEHOUSE
40 Jewry Street, Winchester,
Hampshire, SO23 8RY
www.hoxtonbakehouse.com

164
HUNTER GATHERER COFFEE
249 Albert Road, Southsea, Portsmouth,
Hampshire, PO4 0JR
www.huntergatherer.coffee

165
JOSIE'S
28 Jewry Street, Winchester,
Hampshire, SO23 8SA
www.josieswinecoffee.com

166
KIN + ILK – CAPITAL QUARTER
1 Capital Quarter, Tyndall Street,
Cardiff, CF10 4BZ
www.kinandilk.com

167
MARCH COFFEE
87 South Street, Exeter, Devon, EX1 1EQ
www.marchcoffee.co.uk

168
MILK TEETH
21 Portland Square, Bristol, BS2 8SJ
www.milkteethportlandsq.co.uk

169
MOKOKO COFFEE & BAKERY – SOUTHGATE
7 Dorchester Street, Southgate,
Bath, BA1 1SS
www.mokokocoffee.com

170
MOOR AT 13
13 Fore Street, Kingswear,
Devon, TQ6 0AD

171
NELSON COFFEE
4 Terminus Road, Eastbourne,
East Sussex, BN21 3LP
www.nelsoncoffee.co.uk

172
OFFBEET
Sunnyfields Farm, Jacobs Gutter Lane,
Totten, Southampton,
Hampshire, SO40 9FX
www.offbeetfood.com

173
OLIVE & CO.
Windsor Place, Liskeard,
Cornwall, PL14 4BH
www.olivecocafe.com

174
PELOTON ESPRESSO
76 Cowley Road, Oxford, OX4 1JB
www.pelotonespresso.com

175
PINKMANS
85 Park Street, Bristol, BS1 5PJ
www.pinkmans.co.uk

176
PLAYGROUND COFFEE HOUSE
45 St Nicholas Street, Bristol, BS1 1TP
www.playgroundcoffee.co.uk

177
POLARITY
3 Duke Street Arcade, Cardiff, CF10 1AZ

178
REDROASTER CAFE
1d St James's Street, Brighton,
East Sussex, BN2 1RE
www.redroaster.co.uk

179
RHUBARB & MUSTARD
11 Millbay Road, Plymouth,
Devon, PL1 3LF
www.rhubarbmustard.co.uk

180
ROCKETS & RASCALS
7 Parade, The Barbican, Plymouth,
Devon, PL1 2JL
www.rocketsandrascals.com

181
SPICER+COLE – CLIFTON
9 Princess Victoria Street,
Bristol, BS8 4DX
www.spicerandcole.co.uk

182
SPICER+COLE – GLOUCESTER ROAD
16 The Promenade, Bristol, BS7 8AE
www.spicerandcole.co.uk

183
SPICER+COLE – QUEEN SQUARE
1 Queen Square Avenue,
Bristol, BS1 4JA
www.spicerandcole.co.uk

184
STAR ANISE CAFE
1 Gloucester Street, Stroud,
Gloucestershire, GL5 1QG
www.staranisecafe.co.uk

185
STONEY POINT
15 Montpelier Place, Brighton,
East Sussex, BN1 3BF
www.stoneypoint.co

186
THE CHEEKY BEAN
12-12a Market Place, Shepton Mallet,
Somerset, BA4 5AZ
www.thecheekybean.co.uk

187
THE DISPENSARY KITCHEN
5-6 The Square, Winchester,
Hampshire, SO23 9ES

188
THE FORUM COFFEE HOUSE
3 Forum Buildings, St James Parade,
Bath, BA1 1UG
www.bathforum.co.uk

189
THE LITTLE MAN COFFEE CO. – BRIDGE STREET
Ivor House, Bridge Street,
Cardiff, CF10 2EE
www.littlemancoffee.co.uk

190
THE LITTLE MAN COFFEE CO. – TUDOR LANE
10 Tudor Lane, Riverside,
Cardiff, CF11 6AZ
www.littlemancoffee.co.uk

191
THE NEW ENGLAND COFFEE HOUSE
1 Digbeth Street, Stow-on-the-Wold,
Gloucestershire, GL54 1BN
www.newenglandcoffeehouse.com

192
THE THIRSTY ELEPHANT
12 Cowbridge Road, Pontyclun,
Rhondda Cynon Taf, CF72 9ED
www.thethirstyelephant.com

193
URBAN GROUND – BOLTON ROAD
2a Bolton Road, Eastbourne,
East Sussex, BN21 3JX
www.urbanground.co.uk

194
WATERLOO TEA
21-25 Wyndham Arcade, The Hayes,
Cardiff, CF10 1FH
www.waterlootea.com

MORE GOOD
ROASTERIES
ADDITIONAL BEANS FOR YOUR HOME HOPPER

195
ANVIL COFFEE ROASTERS
The Forge, West Ham Industrial Estate,
Hampshire, RG22 6PW
www.anvilcoffee.co.uk

196
BACK YARD COFFEE
SM Tidy Industrial Estate, Building OPQ,
Unit M, Ditchling Common,
East Sussex, BN6 8SG
www.backyardcoffee.co.uk

197
BEANPRESS COFFEE CO.
The Old Stables, North West Farm,
Winterborne Kingston, Dorset, DT11 9AT
www.beanpress.co.uk

198
BRAZIER COFFEE ROASTERS
Units 10-11, Tonedale Mill Business
Park, Wellington, Somerset, TA21 0AW
www.braziercoffeeroasters.co.uk

199
CLIFTON COFFEE ROASTERS
Unit C2, Island Trade Park,
Bristow Broadway, Avonmouth,
Bristol, BS11 9FB
www.cliftoncoffee.co.uk

200
COALTOWN COFFEE ROASTERS
Foundry Road, Ammanford,
Carmarthenshire, SA18 2LS
www.coaltowncoffee.co.uk

201
COFFEE FACTORY
Unit 3, Samurai Buildings, Seaton
Junction, Axminster, Devon, EX13 7PW
www.thecoffeefactory.co.uk

202
COLONNA COFFEE
Unit 5, Apollo Park, Armstrong Way,
Yate, Bristol, BS37 5AH
www.colonnacoffee.com

203
CRAFT HOUSE COFFEE
Unit F3, Blacklands Farm, Wheatsheaf
Road, Henfield, West Sussex, BN5 9AT
www.crafthousecoffee.co.uk

204
EXE COFFEE ROASTERS
19 Heavitree Road, Exeter, Devon, EX1 2LD
www.execoffeeroasters.co.uk

205
FINCA COFFEE ROASTERS
Unit 101, 20-22 The Grove, Dorchester,
Dorset, DT1 1ST
www.fincacoffee.co.uk

206
FIRE & FLOW
Leckhampton Place, Leckhampton,
Cheltenham, Gloucestershire, GL53 0FB

207
JAMES GOURMET COFFEE
Unit 1, Chase Industrial Estate, Alton Road,
Ross-on-Wye, Herefordshire, HR9 5WA
www.jamesgourmetcoffee.com

208
LUFKIN COFFEE ROASTERS
185 Clare Road, Cardiff, CF11 6RX
www.lufkincoffee.com

209
MANUMIT
Cardiff
www.manumitcoffee.co.uk

210
OLFACTORY COFFEE ROASTERS
The Old Brewery Yard, Lower Treluswell,
Penryn, Cornwall, TR10 9AT
www.olfactorycoffee.co.uk

211
ORIGIN COFFEE ROASTERS
The Roastery, Wheal Vrose Business
Park, Helston, Cornwall, TR13 0FG
www.origincoffee.co.uk

212
PEABERRY COFFEE ROASTERS
60 Basepoint Business & Innovation
Centre, Caxton Close, Andover,
Hampshire, SP10 3QN
www.peaberrycoffee.co.uk

213
QUANTUM COFFEE ROASTERS
58 Bute Street, Cardiff, CF10 5BN
www.quantumroasters.co.uk

214
RAVE COFFEE
Unit 7, Stirling Works, Love Lane,
Cirencester, Gloucestershire, GL7 1YG
www.ravecoffee.co.uk

215
RISING GROUND
Unit 9, Foundry Court, Wadebridge,
Cornwall, PL27 7QN
www.risingground.coffee

216
ROUND HILL ROASTERY
Unit 14 Midsomer Enterprise Park,
Midsomer Norton, Radstock,
Somerset, BA3 2BB
www.roundhillroastery.com

217
THE ROASTING PARTY
Unit 4, Sun Valley Business Park,
Winchester, Hampshire, SO23 0LB
www.theroastingparty.co.uk

218
TRIPLE CO ROAST
11 Charles Street, Stokes Croft, Bristol, BS1 3NN
www.triplecoroast.com

219
UNCOMMON GROUND
South Wales
www.uncommon-ground.co.uk

220
WINCHESTER COFFEE ROASTERS
The Foundry Yard, 4a London Road,
Kings Worthy, Winchester, SO23 7QN
www.winchestercoffeeroasters.co.uk

COFFEE

MEET
our
COMMI

DAN LACEY

Extract Coffee Roasters, Bristol

Dan moved to New Zealand with his family at the age of 14 and picked up the antipodean coffee obsession. An Authorised SCA Trainer (AST) qualified in Barista, Brewing and Sensory Skills with an SCA diploma in coffee, Dan has been a head judge on the UK competition circuit. He's also volunteered at several European Barista Camps and is Extract's regional manager for the South West

RICHARD BLAKE

Yallah Coffee, St Ives

Roasting with the original crew at Extract in the early days, Rich learnt most of what he knows about green coffee, trading, roasting and brewing at the Bristol roastery before launching his own business, Yallah Coffee, in 2014. As a keen surfer and outdoor adventurer, he naturally chose the Cornish countryside in which to house his lovingly restored 1950s roaster.

TEE

CALLUM PARSONS

Fire & Flow, Cotswolds

Topping the South West heats of the UK Barista Championships and taking part in the national competition on numerous occasions, Callum has cemented his place in the speciality industry. Having travelled around the region for one of the country's top indie roasters in a previous role, he knows the best spots for a quality coffee and has launched his own roastery, Fire & Flow, in the Cotswolds.

DAVE STANTON

Crankhouse Coffee, Exeter

After catching the coffee bug down under, Dave returned to the UK eager to master the art of roasting. Fuelling his passion by pouring brews by day, for several years he spent his nights experimenting on his home roaster. He finally took the leap into professional roasting in 2014, launching Crankhouse Coffee from his garage.

Crankhouse stocks speciality coffee shops across the country with its collection of high quality blends and single origin beans and has just moved to a new roastery (with on-site cafe) in Exeter.

TASH MURPHY

Pharmacie Coffee Roasters, Hove

Tash's coffee career began 15 years ago as a barista at the first independent second-wave Brighton coffee roastery, RedRoaster. Tash and Rick Curtis then launched Pharmacie in 2015 at an old car mechanic shop where, with head roaster Carola Mapp, they applied their collective 50-year barista experience to create an eco conscious coffee roastery with slot-roasting and a strong community ethos.

WILL HARRIGAN

River Coffee Roasters, Winchester

Will was a head barista and regional trainer while still at university and even wrote his dissertation on social responsibility in the coffee industry. He later journeyed through South and Central America, living and working with coffee producers, in order to learn about the industry from its roots up. He returned to the UK in 2018 to set up River Coffee, a speciality roastery based in Winchester which works closely with producers at origin.

COFFEE NOTES

Somewhere to save details of specific
brews and beans you've enjoyed

COFFEE NOTES

Somewhere to save details of specific
brews and beans you've enjoyed

INDEX

iNDEX